RENEWED

LUCILLE ZIMMERMAN

RENEWED

Finding Your Inner Happy in
an Overwhelmed World

Abingdon Press / *Nashville*

RENEWED
FINDING YOUR INNER HAPPY IN AN OVERWHELMED WORLD

Library of Congress Cataloging-in-Publication Data has been requested.

ISBN 978-1-4267-4860-8

13 14 15 16 17 18 19 20 21 22—10 9 8 7 6 5 4 3 2 1

MANUFACTURED IN THE UNITED STATES OF AMERICA

Dr. William Saxby—For finding me in the storm and walking me home.

My husband, John—You are the reason I thrive.

Taylor—A daughter is a little girl who grows up to be a friend.

Tucker—Thank you for being a son who listens to my stories and makes me smile.

You are the beings through whom God loved me!

CONTENTS

ACKNOWLEDGMENTS

To my agents: Sandra Bishop, Rachelle Gardner, Greg Johnson. Thank you for believing I had something to say.

To my editors: Lil Copan, Susan Cornell, and Robin Pippin, I'm so lucky to have worked with you.

Becky Johnson, I echo my husband's sentiments: "I'm so glad Becky Johnson is your friend." You give so much encouragement in the way of hope, food, friendship, time, and words.

I'm grateful for the love and support from my family, especially Ruth Rickerby, and Doris and John Zimmerman.

To my Words For The Journey writing group friends. Thank you for showing me that real people write books. To my critique partners: Michele Cushatt, Danica Favorite, and Antje Liley, I'm so grateful for the times we worked in a cozy mountain cabin or on a sunny deck, sipping tea and saying, "Can you believe we get to do this?"

To all my friends on social media, most of whom I've never met, you offered your ideas, encouragement, prayers, and most important, your friendship: Grace Bower, Megan DiMaria, Shelley Hendrix, Robbie Iobst, Brent Johnson,

Natalie Lewis, Heather Lodwick, Katy McKenna, Patricia Raybon, Trish Ruller, Jewell Sample, Sharen Watson, Joan Webb, and so many more.

Alyssa Avant, Kelly Diekmann, and Ingrid Schneider, thank you for your technical help. Deirdre Brouer, thank you for your expertise in the Hebrew language.

To my close friends who prayed, left me alone when I needed to write, and took me out when I needed a break: Diane Bauerle, Maria Brush, Kathy Campbell, Dana and Vicki Christensen, Melba Evans, Sherry Jones, Jan Kalne, Glenda Kirsten, Molly McMillan, Mark and Shelly Montoya, Lindsey O'Connor, Timi Schuessler, Jaci and Ron Snider, Charlotte Stupski, Jim and Jancy Simon, Sue Wilson.

To my professors and mentors at Colorado Christian University. Like the Velveteen Rabbit, you helped me be real. Dr. Frank Ames, Sharon Gipe, Dr. Sherry Parks, Dr. William Saxby, Dr. Ron Welch. Thank you Carson Miles and Dr. Harvey Powers for your clinical supervision. Each of you modeled Christ.

To the real live authors whose writing encouraged me to write true: Chris Bohjalian, Ian Morgan Cron, Dave Cullen, Ken Gire, Dr. Ned Hallowell, Sue Monk Kidd, Tim Madigan, Shauna Niequist, Henri Nouwen, and Mary Pipher.

To my pastors George Kirsten and Todd Lanting: Thank you for holding up the mantle of faith.

WHY RENEWAL THROUGH SELF-CARE?

Peaceful revolutionaries change the world by great effort and small comforts; one hot bath, one morning walk, one quiet act of self-care at a time.

—MARTHA BECK

MY SIXTEEN-YEAR OLD daughter, Taylor, came home for her lunch break. When she heard music blasting, she took the stairs two at a time and pushed open my bedroom door. What she found was her mom dancing in the room to Enrique Iglesias, who was belting out a Latin hip-hop beat: "So don't turn out the lights . . . eeh-ah eeh-ah ay ay." "Mom," she laughed, "What are you doing?" I'm sure Taylor didn't expect to find me singing and dancing. That simple act of listening to happy music created a fun memory for both of us, and my happiness spread to my daughter. This is often the way it is with self-care—as you take time out to refresh yourself, the benefits naturally flow to others.

Before I made the decision to go back to school and earn a master's degree in counseling, my life was consumed with the business of life: raising kids, teaching Bible studies, running a home business, and organizing a ministry at our church that arranged meals for people in need. Life was filled with a lot of rushing around, answering phone calls, holding workshops, driving the kids to their activities, and delivering supplies to my customers.

Not only was I rushing but also in my insecurity I was always trying to please others. I thought the more I did to help others, the more they would like me. When I went back to school, my busy life came to a screeching halt. My phone stopped ringing. My car stayed in the garage. Except for the classes I took, every day looked the same: me, a book and highlighter in hand, reading. The only thing that changed was my location—sometimes I read on the back porch, sometimes the living room.

The material I read often surprised and upset me. Gone was the happy smile on my face, trying to hide anxiety and low-level depression. Gone was fooling myself. I had gone back to school to help others, but I began to see the dysfunctional patterns reflected within me, within the home in which I was raised.

Most of us assume our life is normal and that the smile on our face is genuine, until something stops us. A decision or a life incident causes the smile to drop and us to examine our lives and our family-of-origin dynamics. Counselors call this a "trigger"—when painful events evoke a strong bodily or emotional response. Most people have heard a song or caught a scent that transported them back in time to a painful memory. They may suddenly feel scared or sad in the present, even though the event happened long ago.

As I immersed myself into my studies at breakneck speed, anxious to get all my emotional junk out and to fix myself as soon as possible, I kept getting triggered. And I was counseled to slow down and do self-care in order to lessen the feeling of being overwhelmed.

Self-care? The counselor may as well have been speaking another language! I had no idea what self-care was. Most of us who face those triggers learn quickly that if we are not deliberate about extreme self-care, we quickly burn out. Now, in my work with clients, I realize they come to me because they are stressed, too—they are carrying the weight of family and church and work obligations, and have no idea how to nurture their physical, emotional, and spiritual selves. When I mention self-care, they look at me in the same puzzled way I once looked at my counselor.

You may have lived a difficult life or you may have an emotionally draining job. Or maybe you are reading this book just to begin to pay more attention to giving care to yourself so that you don't suffer burnout. It doesn't matter where you begin. This book invites you to attend to yourself in the midst of a stressful life.

My passion as a counselor and writer is to help people like you learn positive responses to coping with stress and to give yourself permission to care for yourself in order to minimize the negative effects on you and on others. So, let's get started!

EFFECTS OF STRESS

Let's face it: women hold a lot of stress. Research has shown that the effects of stress are more extreme for women than for men. Women release more stress chemicals, and these hormones remain longer in a woman's body than a man's. Women also appear to be more susceptible to the physical symptoms of stress because of gender differences in brain processing. Overall, women tend to be more sensitive to stress, and the stress response lasts longer in the female body than in the male one. Ninety-five percent of all office visits to doctors are for stress-related ailments (McClellan and Hamilton, *So Stressed*).

Don't think you're stressed? Take a simple test. Do any of the following affect you?

- Nervousness or anxiety
- Sadness or depression
- Anger
- Fatigue
- Sleep disorders
- Lack of interest, motivation, or energy
- Inability to concentrate
- Headaches

- Muscle tension in neck and shoulders
- Upset stomach, bloating, appetite changes
- Dizziness or faintness
- Tightness in chest
- Reduced sexual desire
- Skin problems—rashes, acne, hives
- Aches and pain
- Menstrual irregularity
- Constipation or diarrhea
- Hair loss or dullness

Maybe you picked up this book because you are stressed out. Maybe you think that it's a small issue you want to resolve and that it doesn't affect you that much, but the long-term effects of your determined grim-smile life may require a high price. The long-term effects of stress for women are many. Isn't it time to take care of yourself?

BENEFITS OF SELF-CARE

Maybe you feel guilty taking care of yourself, looking at your life, wanting to make significant changes. Maybe you feel your family or church or workplace wouldn't understand. Many women feel that they would be selfish to even consider self-care.

But self-care is *not* selfish. Self-care is about taking control of your own health and happiness. By being in control you stay healthy and put yourself in charge of making sure you have a good quality of life. Taking good care of yourself means the people in your life receive the best of you rather than what is left of you.

When Jesus told people to love their neighbor as themselves, he was presupposing that people would love themselves. If we don't love ourselves, we are violating that commandment just the same as when we don't love others. Alternately, if we only care for ourselves without caring for others, that is selfishness. But loving ourselves—and others—is good and godly.

Without nurturing their own energy, passion, and health, and without setting limits on their own activity, women are useful to no one. Remember the flight attendant's instructions to passengers to strap on their own breathing apparatus before attending to others on the airplane? Women need to prioritize their emotional, spiritual, and physical health before always rushing to help others first.

The afternoon my daughter caught me singing started out with my putting a little fun into my day. In fact, it was a deliberate session of self-care, with music as the relaxing and calming balm. Yet, as Taylor and I lay on my bed and began to sing the lyrics together, a typical day became an extraordinary day as my own self-care spilled over to lighten my daughter's day as well. As we focused on the particular way Enrique pronounced the words of the song—"You. Can. Take. My. Breath-ay-way"—we lost ourselves in laughter. It was a memory I will always treasure.

Now is the time for self-care. Dr. Phil is famous for saying, "Life isn't a dress rehearsal." So many people live their lives thinking that someday is the day they will stop and enjoy their lives.

IT ONLY TAKES A LITTLE TO SHINE A LOT

Right about now, some of you may be thinking, *Oh great, now one more thing on my to-do list. One more thing to make me feel guilty when I can't accomplish it.* Fun, rest, nurture, self-care, stillness, quiet, reflection, focus—whatever you want to call it, my goal is for you to see that self-care is easy; but it does not come naturally to most of us.

There's a Dutch word that captures what I want to convey in this book. The term is *gezellig* (heh-SELL-ick). Dutch people will tell you that the word cannot be translated—its meaning is a combination of cozy, quaint, nice, friendly, comfortable, relaxing, enjoyable, and gregarious. I pray that as a result of reading this book you will fill your life with *gezellig* moments.

The aim of this book is to help you understand the importance of putting yourself on your to-do list, and to provide basic steps to help you get you started. You may be a go-getter, but remember to start small. As you read, consider what little things you could insert into your daily routine. In the following chapters I've listed great ways to begin small, and have included a notes page in the back of the book for you to use to jot down ideas as they come to mind.

And if you're worried that self-care will be expensive, don't be. This isn't a book about day spas and expensive vacations. Self-care doesn't have to be radical or expensive. Start where you are and do what you can. You will be surprised at how effective small steps are in helping you learn to care for yourself.

Have you ever heard of the "lipstick effect"? It is a theory that states that when the economy goes into a recession or a depression, the sale of lipstick increases. The "lipstick effect" is a term that can be traced back to the Great Depression: in the four years from 1929 to 1933, the sale of cosmetics rose. Theorists believe that people continue to spend money on small luxuries during times of economic or emotional stress in order to buoy their spirits. The same thing happened after the terrorist attacks of 9/11—lipstick sales increased.

Not everyone enjoys the lift that lipstick brings, but there are small items you can buy, view, or even window-shop that will give you a truckload of happiness. Maybe it's a pretty journal or a beautiful pen. Maybe it's a frilly blouse that makes you feel ultrafeminine, or perhaps it's a pumpkin-caramel latte that feels warm and comforting. Even if the item is small, the fact that you took time to buy and enjoy it affirms your worth to yourself.

Many of the ideas I'll be sharing in this book stem from the latest research on happiness and positive psychology, so there is clinical evidence to back them up. These simple ideas have the capacity to change your life in a big way. Thomas Merton said, "Happiness is not a matter of intensity but of balance and order and rhythm and harmony" (*No Man Is an Island*, 127). My book is by no means exhaustive, but it offers ways for you to incorporate balance, order, rhythm, and harmony. And best of all, it gives you permission to take care of yourself.

If you chose this book, at some deep level you must know that it is time to consider your own health and that you are ready to enjoy your life and your family and your deep spiritual values and find your way to that beautiful word *balance*.

I applaud you for recognizing that, and I look forward to sharing in the pages and days to come life-changing strategies to help you better care for yourself. Maybe you'll even put Enrique on your stereo and sing, "You. Can. Take. My. Breath-ay-way."

CHAPTER 1

RENEWED THROUGH EMOTIONAL SELF-CARE

People are like stained glass windows—
the true beauty can be seen only when
there is light within.
—ELISABETH KÜBLER-ROSS

AS I BEGAN TO WORK on revisions for this book, I noticed when I was walking into my office that my chest was tight, and I realized that I had avoided getting started because I was scared. I said to myself out loud, "Lu, it's OK. Just take it step by step. You don't need to be scared. These are just revisions, and you already wrote a whole book. This is the last set of steps. You can do this."

As I said the words, instantly my body felt lighter, and a feeling of joy washed over me.

How we think about ourselves and talk to ourselves is very important. Most of us don't need clinical proof showing us that feeling good has a healing effect on our bodies and that our mind-set can influence immunity and the rate at which we heal from injury or illness. There is a powerful link between emotional outlook and physical health. This chapter has the potential to improve your life, and with just a little time and practice you can make major shifts in how you think about and talk to yourself. This chapter will help you understand how the things you say and believe affect your feelings and behavior—and how to make small, positive changes.

WHAT YOU TELL YOURSELF AFFECTS YOUR EMOTIONAL HEALTH

Basically, it boils down to this: if you say and think you're stupid, your emotions and actions will bear that out. If you say and believe you have value and that you always give life your best, your feelings and actions follow.

What you tell yourself matters.

People can react differently to the same event. Counselors call this tendency to see what we want to see "confirmation bias." For instance, let's say Roger asks Susan out on a date. Susan says no. Roger could say, "I'm a no-good lout for all time," or he could say, "Susan was in a rejecting mood that day." Maybe he could say, "Susan's response was about Susan, not about me." Just read each of those short sentences of Roger's out loud, and notice the shift in the way each can make a person feel.

Back when I was selling scrapbook supplies from my home, I had an experience with giving too much credence to someone's negative response to me. I had sold supplies to a customer, and invested in supporting her emotionally; I knew she was dying of cancer. I went out of my way to give her freebie album supplies that I knew she would appreciate. Many of my customers had also gotten to know her and care for her. When she died, I sent an e-mail asking my customers to keep her husband in their prayers. I had forgotten to remove her e-mail address from my group e-mail list, and her hurting husband received the e-mail and responded with intense anger.

I was so devastated that day that I vowed never to send an e-mail again. I sent him a note of apology, but I continued to lambaste myself over it. I gave more credence to what someone said about me than what I knew to be true about myself.

Instead of lambasting myself, I should have considered whether I had done something wrong, examined what I had done for my friend and her family and realized the words directed at me were sourced in her husband's pain, and ultimately dismissed what he said about me.

In situations such as these, one of the most helpful questions I've learned to ask myself is, *What is this person telling you about himself or herself?* All of our actions and words are reflections of our past experiences. They are evidence of the lens through which we see the world. When people blow up or overreact, it usually isn't about what we did wrong but about how much those people are hurting or how affected they are by their own emotional histories. The more we are able to back off and see a bigger picture, the more we stop allowing others to direct our lives.

STOP LETTING PEOPLE PUT "CAT HAIR" ON YOU

A person with a strong sense of self doesn't absorb the negative emotions and projections of others or give others more power and authority in his or her life than he or she should. One of my counselor friends told me, "Stop letting people put their cat hair on you!" In a mock gesture she brushed the cat hair off my shoulder. Don't automatically assume that just because someone is mad at you, you are at fault. You don't have to absorb the reactions of others. Step back, brush off the cat hair, and give yourself permission to evaluate what occurred from a more objective standpoint.

People who don't have a strong sense of self, or ego strength, may find it difficult to stop letting others' opinions matter more than their own. Many women in their thirties, forties, and fifties are walking around without a strong sense of self. If the person I'm describing sounds all too familiar, and is in fact you, the next chapter, "Renewed Through Figuring Out Who You Are," will be helpful as you begin building up your ego strength—your sense of yourself and your worth.

AFFIRMATIONS CAN CHANGE THE WAY YOU FEEL AND REACT

I had no idea how much a list of affirmations posted on my bathroom mirror could influence my life for the better. As I did my own emotional work in school, I read one or two affirmations aloud each day ("I don't have to make everyone happy today" or "It's OK if I make a mistake"), and over time those words made a huge impact. Your brain believes what you tell it, even if you are saying it silently.

Here is a list of some affirmations that have the power to make a big difference in how you react to life. You may want to pick out one or two to read aloud each day.

- I do not have to feel guilty just because someone else does not like what I do, say, think, or feel.
- It's OK for me to feel angry and to express it in responsible ways.
- I do not have to assume full responsibility for making decisions, particularly where others share responsibility for making the decision.
- I have the right to say, "I don't know."
- I have the right to say no without feeling guilty.
- I have the right to say, "I don't understand," without feeling stupid.
- I do not have to apologize or give reasons when I say no.
- I have the right to ask others to do things for me.
- I have the right to refuse requests that others make of me.
- I have the right to tell others when I think they are manipulating me, conning me, or treating me unfairly.
- I have the right to refuse additional responsibilities without feeling guilty.

- I have the right to tell others when their behavior annoys me.
- I do not have to compromise my personal integrity.
- I have the right to make mistakes and to be responsible for them; I have the right to be wrong.
- I do not have to be liked, admired, or respected by everyone for everything I do.

WOMEN WHO DO WHAT THEY LOVE ARE HAPPIEST

Did you know that doing what you love and doing a lot of it is a secret to happiness? Best-selling author and researcher Marcus Buckingham was surprised with research he did at Gallup that showed that women's happiness had plummeted over the last forty years—the exact opposite of men. He devoted himself to figuring out what made the happiest women happy. He found that the happiest women tended to focus on the few areas where they excelled. If a woman loved marathons, she didn't waste her time on home decorating. If she enjoyed studying rocket science, she didn't focus on entertaining friends. You get the idea (*Find Your Strongest Life*, 17, 96, 138, 163).

Not only did she do what she loved, she also did something Buckingham calls "catch and cradle": she noticed herself doing what she loved. For instance, if you're with your friends—say, a writing group that you love—sit back, sip some tea, and really pay attention to how much you enjoy writing and being with your friends. Take a mental picture (or an actual one) of the magic moment. Whether your snapshot is real or tucked away in your memory, taking an occasion to savor what you enjoy is a vital step in self-care.

It makes sense that if you want to feel good about yourself, you will spend the vast majority of your time doing what you love.

What activities do you really enjoy? When do you lose track of time because you are doing something so enjoyable that you are caught up in a sense of timelessness?

Researchers call this "flow," and I'll talk more about it later in the book. When do you feel you are doing what you were born to do? My friend Danica experiences much pleasure in the simple art of knitting. For Michele, it's running a quiet trail; and for Antje, it's reading comics. Recently I was at a speaker training and heard comedian Bob Stromberg say that he often sits in his sauna with music and gets so caught up in thinking of creative ideas that he won't realize an hour has gone by. If you want to be happy, do what you're good at and do what you love. Not sure what your strengths or interests are? There are a lot of strengths-finder books and online tests. Try one. A starting place is *StrengthsFinder 2.0* by Tom Rath.

YOUR SOCIAL NETWORK DETERMINES HAPPINESS

Another key to emotional self-care is to choose your networks wisely. It's important to spend time around others who are behaving and acting in ways that you want to mirror and have mirrored in your life. Your brain automatically "picks up" signals from those around you in ways you might never consciously realize. In fact, you become like those you spend time with, so it pays to be intentional in your choices of friends and mentors.

In the book *Connected: The Surprising Power of Our Social Networks and How They Shape Our Lives*, authors Nicholas A. Christakis and James H. Fowler describe how we are connected to everyone by six degrees of separation, but we influence and are influenced by those within three degrees of separation. That means people I don't even know have the power to affect me (for example, a friend of a friend). Studies have shown that obesity and divorce spread through social networks. Choose your social network wisely and you'll find yourself buoyed by positive support and encouragement.

One of the greatest discoveries of neuroscience in the last decade came when scientists accidentally discovered mirror neurons. You probably remember from biology class that a neuron is a brain cell. Brain cells transmit electrical and chemical signals, and connect to others to form networks. Scientists estimate there are one hundred billion neurons in the human brain. For hundreds of years, scientists thought the brain was rigid and permanent. They also assumed the brain could never grow new cells. Only in the last decade have scientists discovered that the brain is pliable, plastic, moldable, and that it can grow.

A team of Italian researchers placed electrodes in the front of a monkey's brain in order to study the neurons involved as the monkey cracked open a peanut and put it in his mouth. During a break, one of the scientists cracked a peanut for himself, and the monkey's brain made the same signal; the exact neurons fired when the monkey watched the action as when the monkey did it himself. Thus, the neurons "mirror" the behavior of another, as though the observer were doing the activity as well.

SMILING CHANGES THE WAY YOU FEEL

Can you tell a real smile from a fake one? Did you know that biting down on a pencil as you smile actually makes you happy? That's because it works the same muscles as a genuine smile, or "Duchenne smile," which involves both voluntary and involuntary contraction from two muscles, the zygomatic major (raising the corners of the mouth) and the orbicularis oculi (raising the cheeks and producing crow's feet around the eyes). A fake smile, often the one we use when our picture is being taken, only contracts the zygomatic major. So when you're looking through photo albums and magazines and you want to know who is really happy, look for the people with crinkles around their eyes, not the ones who are simply stretching their lips across their face.

What's going on in the brain that creates these two different smiles? Scientists have discovered that these two types of smiles are actually controlled by two completely different parts of the brain. When a patient with damage to the motor cortex on the brain's left hemisphere attempts to smile, the smile is asymmetrical, with the right side of the smile not moving, as it should. However, when that same patient spontaneously laughs, the smile is normal with no asymmetry. The motor cortex controls the fake smile, whereas the limbic system (the emotional center of the brain) controls emotion-related movement, such as the Duchenne smile.

You can proactively manipulate your brain into being happy by giving yourself a small treat; for example, a funny video clip, a day out with fun friends, or remembering some of your favorite happy experiences. Matt Harding made Internet fame dancing in more than seventy countries on all seven continents. Whenever I find myself in a slump, I jump over to YouTube and the clip titled "Where the Hell is Matt? 2008." Seeing people from all over the world dancing and smiling with Matt never fails to lift my mood.

Taking a few moments to make yourself happy is a wonderful and creative form of self-care. Just as you feed your body good nutrients, you can nourish your soul by feeding your brain good, uplifting thoughts and pictures. About once a month, I go to lunch and a movie with my friends Charlotte and Sue. The first time we did it, we went to see the movie *Mamma Mia*. In order to get us in the mood, I brought along my ABBA CD. We sang and laughed all the way to the theater. From that point on, we dubbed ourselves "the *Mamma Mias*," and we refer to our monthly outings as "*Mamma Mia* days."

What kind of uplifting activities—*Mamma Mia* days—are you giving yourself?

EXTREME THINKING AFFECTS YOUR EMOTIONAL STATE

Ever find yourself saying things like, "Oh no, that's the worst!" or "Oh, how awful!"? Do you catastrophize things? Or maybe you go to extremes, saying things like, "I never get what I want," or, "They always leave without me."

Black-and-white thinking like this is common for people pleasers. It also recurs for trauma survivors, who tend to see the world in extremes—as all or nothing. Perhaps they had to be hypervigilant in order to prevent repercussions from demanding and abusive parents. But when we catastrophize, the brain releases various stress chemicals, including cortisol. Higher and more prolonged levels of cortisol in the bloodstream have negative effects, such as:

- Impaired cognitive performance
- Suppressed thyroid function
- Blood sugar imbalances such as hyperglycemia
- Decreased bone density
- Decrease in muscle tissue
- High blood pressure
- Lower immunity and inflammatory responses in the body, slowed wound healing, and other health consequences
- Increased abdominal fat, which is associated with a greater amount of health problems (heart attacks, strokes, high cholesterol) than fat deposited in other areas of the body

If you find yourself going to extreme responses, make a small change. Try to exchange knee-jerk negative responses with a sense of curiosity. Instead of engaging in extreme thinking, teach yourself to say, "Hmm, this is interesting," or, "I wonder what's going to happen?"

Other negative signal words detrimental to emotional health are *ought*, *should*, or *must*. In future chapters we'll look at how beliefs like perfectionism, impossible expectations, learned helplessness, fear of losing control, filling in the blanks, and unrealistic comparisons all work against our emotional well-being, whereas opening new pathways of thinking can help us become healthier and happier people. In the next chapter, we'll start with one of the basics and bedrocks of living renewed: figuring out who you are.

CHAPTER 2

RENEWED THROUGH FIGURING OUT WHO YOU ARE

Cherish your visions; cherish your ideals; cherish the music that stirs in your heart, the beauty that forms in your mind, the loveliness that drapes your purest thoughts, for out of them will grow delightful conditions, all heavenly environment; of these if you but remain true to them, your world will at last be built.

—JAMES ALLEN

 PROBLEMS AND STRESS are a regular part of life. But have you noticed that some people seem better equipped to deal with difficult relationships and the stressors of life? For example, I used to wake up and wonder where the day's problems were going to take me, and felt trapped by poor interpersonal boundaries, whereas my friend could be in the midst of all sorts of drama and tension in his workplace and have none of these struggles. He would smile, giggle, and say lightheartedly, "I love my job."

People who have a strong sense of self have a zest for living; they are able to handle stress and bounce back from adversity. They have a sense of meaning in their lives. They are flexible and able to adapt to change. They have a healthy balance between work and play, and they have self-confidence and high self-esteem.

Having a healthy sense of self also means having an accurate, realistic, and authentic awareness of who you are, and being able to see your inherent worthiness. I'm not talking about the kind of ego that causes a person to think he or she is better than others. Instead, someone with a strong sense of self recognizes his or her strengths, weaknesses, values, likes, and dislikes. A healthy sense of self is required for effective communication, strong interpersonal relations, and the ability to show empathy for others. Those with a strong sense of self have self-esteem and positive self-awareness but also have a humility about themselves before God (see Micah 6:8).

DEVELOPING A POSITIVE SENSE OF SELF

We develop our identity (our sense of self) in light of what is reflected back to us. If a parent didn't light up when we walked into a room, we probably did not grow up feeling special. Children who grow up in a chaotic or alcoholic home have little time to attend to themselves; they are too busy attending to others. For a painful look at what happens to children when a parent fails to attune to them by speaking and showing facial reactions, see the clip on YouTube called "The Still Face Experiment." A mother is shown having a normal interaction with her baby. She coos, mimics, claps hands, widens her eyes, speaks softly, repeats, and so on. Then the researcher asks the mother to remain still and show no emotion when the young child tries to interact. Within seconds the child grows frantic and cries. You can imagine what happens to a child who grows up with an absent, depressed, or substance-abusing parent.

Children who didn't get a sense of self don't suddenly develop one just because they get older and turn into adults. Sometimes wounded little girls and boys live in grown-up bodies. These are the ones threatening others in the workplace, having affairs, suffering from road rage, over-spending, and succumbing to addictions. They are doing all these things because they didn't get to express real feelings, and they didn't get all the love and nurturing they needed. They didn't learn to ask for their needs to be met, and they didn't learn how to meet these needs themselves.

Often I meet with clients who say they are good at reading people. They say it as if the trait were genetic. I tell them, "You had to develop that skill. You had to be able to predict when Mom was going to get drunk or Dad was going to explode." Alice Miller wrote a book with the misleading title *The Drama of the Gifted Child.* Instead of being a book about intelligent children, it is about children who grow up hyperaware (consciously or otherwise) of the wishes of their parents and who have such a strong desire to fulfill these wishes that they lose track of themselves and their own identity. Gifted children don't learn to discover their "true self" because they are motivated by pleasing those around them.

There are certain types of people who decide to become caretakers and rescuers, and it makes sense that they often pick careers where their role can be reenacted. Of course not all doctors, nurses, counselors, and police officers come from trauma-filled homes, but many do. Many learn to take care of others without ever putting themselves on the list. Years ago I read a book about a nurse who asked a friend to come over to help her move. When the friend asked what she could do, the nurse said she could pack her closet. The friend said, "There's nothing in here." Hanging in the closet were a few T-shirts and a couple pairs of pants. It was at that moment that the nurse realized the way she was living wasn't normal. She had put herself so far down the list that she didn't even have a wardrobe.

Some grown-ups never develop a positive ego because they don't place themselves around people who treat them well; they continue to play the parts that dysfunctional people prescribe to them, catering to the demands of others and never growing into their own identity.

LEARNED HELPLESSNESS

People without a healthy sense of self focus on pleasing others. They give their power away, they compare themselves to others, and they rarely consider their own desires and passions. By focusing on what they think will please others, they don't live the life God designed for them. Theirs is an inauthentic life based on fear and "shoulds." They find it difficult to do something kind for themselves.

I think back to a time in my life when I was living in a strange city and working the night shift at a hospital, where I shared an office with the security guard. This man would call his wife and subject her to horrible verbal abuse, calling her every foul name imaginable. I listened to this diatribe night after night without saying anything. One of his duties was to walk me to my car in a dangerous neighborhood. One night he tried to kiss me. I pulled away but did not report it to his supervisor because I was too insecure and too afraid.

Why would I allow myself to be treated this way without doing something about it? At the time, I did not have a strong sense of self. I didn't think I had the right to speak up.

Maybe you too are starting to recognize that you might not have a healthy sense of who you are. Without a strong sense of self, you can feel powerless. In 1967, the legendary psychologist Martin Seligman did a series of experiments that led him to coin the term "learned helplessness." In one experiment a German shepherd lay in the corner of a metal box, whimpering as he received painful shocks. The dog could have easily moved to the other side of the box where no shocks were being given, but the dog did not budge. That's because he had learned to be helpless in a prior experiment. A few days earlier, a harness had restrained the animal as he received the shocks. He could not get free of the harness, nor could he get away in order to escape the painful shocks. The dog learned that there was no way out, no way to make the pain stop, no options, and no control.

Below are some basic questions designed to help you understand where you are on the self-worth scale. Check the ones that apply to you.

Do you:

- Overspend, overeat, or overindulge
- Expect others to read your mind and meet your needs
- Withhold success from yourself
- Ignore your deepest desires but seek to fulfill the desires of others
- Ignore your real emotions and put on a "happy" face
- Push yourself beyond reasonable limits
- Allow others to emotionally, physically, or sexually abuse you
- Deflect compliments
- Say yes because you can't say no
- Avoid time alone
- Overexhaust yourself because of your need to feel important, needed, or worthy
- Fear emotional intimacy
- Try to do it all yourself, never asking for help
- Try to appear perfect

Or do you:

- Take time for yourself
- Allow yourself to make mistakes and be open about your weaknesses

- Ask for your needs to be met from a place of vulnerability
- Spend time with friends
- Rest
- Play
- Exercise
- Eat well
- Spend money wisely
- Pursue your dreams
- Share honestly with others
- Enjoy and make time to be intimate with those you love
- Forgive
- Allow others to be disappointed in you
- Appropriately express emotions, including anger and sadness
- Tell others what they mean to you
- Be present for your children
- Receive love from others
- Say yes and no
- Create a powerful support system for yourself
- Celebrate accomplishments, big and small

If you had more check marks on the first list than on the second one, you may want to do some work to discover more about who you are so that you can start living a life based on your true self rather than on the false one who is living for others. The number of check marks can feel overwhelming. But take heart, you are capable of growth and change. And remember, renewal can begin through taking small steps, making small but effective changes.

THE JOURNEY OF FIGURING
OUT WHO YOU ARE

As a counselor I am allowed into the very private parts of people's lives, and I consider it a holy privilege. Some of these individuals are extremely negative about and critical of their perceived weaknesses, and are unable to identify their strengths. I have many tools at my disposal when helping a client figure out who she or he is.

When I recognize someone lacking ego strength, I ask simple questions like, "What is your favorite color?" "What's your favorite kind of music (movie, book)?" or "What do you do with your spare time?" Then I move into more complex questions, such as, "What do you do to try to win the attention of important people in your life?" or "What question are you most afraid I'll ask?" My favorite one of all is when I hand them my furry wand that makes a *brrriiiiinnnng* sound and ask, "If you could wave this wand and something could be different, what would it be?" How would you answer these questions?

One of my favorite tools as a counselor is to ask my clients to watch certain movies and then write in a journal about any characters they find themselves relating to. The movie *What's Eating Gilbert Grape*, starring Leonardo DiCaprio and Johnny Depp, is one I recommend a lot. It's the story of an adolescent boy who is trying to find himself in the midst of a complicated family. After his father's suicide, the teenage Gilbert gives all his attention to his morbidly obese mother, a sister who accidentally starts fires, a mentally challenged brother, and an unhappily married woman. Gilbert has no time to attend to himself. Eventually Gilbert explodes with unexpected but understandable rage. He finds himself and discovers life, love, and freedom.

REWRITING BELIEFS ABOUT YOURSELF

I sometimes ask clients to draw a giant egg shape on a large piece of paper. I ask them to draw their earliest trauma memories using symbols or stick figures and to separate each picture by drawing a line or compartment around it. (Drawing figures incorporates the right side of the brain.) Not everyone has what counselors call "Big T" traumas— things like abuse, family death, and so on—but still, everyone has major events that influence the course of their life. These events include things such as moves, divorcing parents, or being teased on the playground; those things affect us.

In this exercise clients draw and emotionally experience their most difficult memories until they get near the top of their "trauma egg." Then they write out the overarching belief that they have concluded about life. Some might write, "People who love me leave me," "No one could love me," or, "The world is not safe." (Remember confirmation bias: we scan our world and confirm our beliefs about life.) Then they come in and tell me about these memories. We discuss the rules of and the roles they had to play in their family of origin. We talk about caregivers and what they did, both good and bad. Then, in the safety of the relationship, we rewrite a new belief: "I deserve love (or "I am lovable and valuable"), and I am of immense worth to God."

TELL YOUR STORY

Another way I help clients grow into their identity is by
having them talk about and write their stories. By sharing
their stories and being able to look at themselves realistically, clients are able to identify and accept their strengths
and weaknesses. Many clients swing from one end of the
pendulum to another: from self-hate to a narcissistic self-
love. Both ends of those self-perceptions have their roots in
psychological wounding. Sound mental health is about seeing one's self realistically. Counselors can help by mirroring
back love that the grown child may not have received. "A
corrective emotional experience" is the clinical term for what
happens. Counselors also pace the storytelling so that
clients will not remain overwhelmed or underwhelmed with
emotions. The counselor gently points out things like, "You
just told me that awful story with a smile on your face," or,
"When you told me how your dad hurt you, you did so with
no emotion." Doing the hard work of growing can be slow
going and painful because clients are being exposed directly
to their emotional pain. They are also grieving parts of
their history.

When you are delving into your own storytelling, you need
to take special care. Pay attention to the times you are hun-
gry, angry, lonely, or tired (HALT). These are times when you
need to pay special attention to your needs. Increase self-
care by focusing on what you want, need, and feel. As people grow and heal, they learn to recognize when they are
being triggered, and they learn to ask for motherly, fatherly,
or friendly bits of love from others.

A friend once sent me a metaphor she found helpful: when a negative emotion comes up, she says to it, "Welcome, old friend, I know how to care for you." Then she uses her nurturing skills, like a mother embracing a baby, to calm the upset-child part of her self. She relaxes into God's nurturing love and allows herself to just breathe.

It may seem hard to believe, but when people developing a sense of self are transforming and growing, they sometimes lose their identity altogether for a while. When they stop being who everyone else wants them to be, but before they figure out who they are, they may feel empty and confused. For example, I can't tell you the number of times I've heard a client say, "I don't know what to wear anymore." Perhaps the client has come to realize she doesn't have to bare cleavage in order to gain attention and worth from a man, but she stares blankly and wonders, "What would someone like me wear?" I always see that as a good sign, even though it is unsettling to the client. Here is someone finally gaining ego strength—something that should have happened when she was much younger.

FOLLOW YOUR OWN NORTH STAR

Psychologist and author Mary Pipher says girls are raised to look for praise and rewards from others instead of learning internal validation. Pipher writes:

> The most important question for every client is "Who are you?" I am not as interested in an answer as I am in teaching a process that the girl can use for the rest of her life. The process involves looking within to find a true core of self,

acknowledging unique gifts, accepting feelings, not just the socially acceptable ones, and making deep and firm decisions about values and meaning. The process includes knowing the difference between thinking and feeling, between immediate gratification and long-term goals, and between her own voice and the voice of others. . . .

I often use the North Star as a metaphor. I tell clients, "You are in a boat that is being tossed around by the winds of the world. The voices of your parents, your teachers, your friends and the media can blow you east, then west, then back again. To stay on course you must follow your own North Star, your sense of who you truly are. Only by orienting north can you keep from being blown all over the sea." (*Reviving Ophelia*, 254)

How do you know when you have developed a strong sense of self? For me it happened when I got to tell my story to a safe mentor; I grieved and got mad when love was reflected back to me, and then my depression and anxiety went away.

As you begin to understand your values, strengths, and passions, trust them as a source of meaning and direction. They will take you to your true self. Keep a journal and talk with safe people. It's exciting to find the true you!

Here are components of a healthy self-concept in the form of questions to consider, write journal responses to, or talk to a counselor about. [The following are adapted from www.instepministries.com.]

Strong Boundaries
- Can I say no?
- Can I let good things in and keep bad things out?

- Do I respect and honor the boundaries of others? (We will talk more about honoring boundaries in the next chapter.)

Healthy Partners
- Do I know what I need in order to thrive in a relationship?
- Do I know what key needs I have that my partner can help me meet?
- Have I defined what I can live with and what I can't live without in a relationship?
- Do I know what I will not tolerate?
- Am I willing to grow with my partner?

Interactions with Others
- Do I engage in many activities that bring me peace and joy?
- Am I being me at all times?
- Do I use power, sex, or money to attract people?
- Do I expect everyone to be attracted to me?
- Do I require attention from everyone?
- Do I compare myself to others?
- Have I surrounded myself with a loving, vibrant community of emotionally healthy people?

New Relationship Patterns
- Do I recognize emotionally available people?
- Do I recognize godly, spiritual people?
- Do I recognize kind people?
- Do I set limits with emotionally toxic people?

- Do I see people for who they are, not for who I want them to be?
- Do I have numerous role models?

Vision and Passion

- Am I clear about my life dreams?
- Am I living my life to the fullest?
- Do I know the type of work I am passionate about, and am I doing it?
- Do I know how I want to spend my time?
- Do I know what I contribute to others?
- Is my life integrated?
- Is what people see who I really am?
- Do I know what legacy I want to leave behind?
- Are my finances in order and manageable?

Personal Faith

- Do I have a close relationship with God, and do other believers surround me?
- Do I make time for prayer, study, and quiet?
- Do I trust God to lead my life and with the timing?
- Am I truly happy and living a full life in the present?
- Do I draw my value and worth from God?
- Do I feel that God loves me?

New Dating Patterns

- Do I see my partner for who he or she is, not for his or her potential?
- Am I having fun in the dating process?

- Do I limit my time together in a new relationship?
- Do I engage sexually in relationships that are not long term and committed?

In the next chapter we will address a crucial concept to understand about self-care: healthy boundaries.

CHAPTER 3

RENEWED THROUGH HEALTHY BOUNDARIES

I don't know the key to success, but
the key to failure is trying to please
everybody.

—BILL COSBY

I WENT TO SEE A MOVIE for the second time because I enjoyed it so much the first time. I wanted to catch all the nuances. Unfortunately, there were two couples who talked throughout the feature. I tried to "shhh" them a few times, with no effect. When it was over, I calmly told them that their talking had made my experience unpleasant. I didn't say it in a mean or aggressive way, but I felt it was important to my boundaries to verbalize my disappointment. What would you have done? If you are like many women, especially Christian women, you keep quiet in situations like this. Maybe you confuse boundary setting with being aggressive and rude.

When I began my counseling internship, my supervisor told me to buy the book *Boundaries*, written by Henry Cloud and John Townsend. *Not another book to read*, I thought to myself. I love reading, but I was already swamped with books I wanted to finish. Then he added, "You'll be recommending and referring to this book more than any other in your practice." He was right. Almost every single problem clients bring to a counselor has something to do with an overreaching of or inability to set clear boundaries.

WHAT IS A BOUNDARY?

The word *boundary* in the American Heritage Dictionary is defined as "an indicated border or limit." In relationships, boundaries are often defined as the line that indicates where one person ends and the other begins. Boundaries keep a person from being controlled, manipulated, and abused. They are the physical, emotional, and sexual limits we set in relationships. They make it possible for us to separate our thoughts and feelings from those of others, and to take responsibility for our behaviors. They enable us to say no, and to accept limits from others.

People with healthy boundaries have developed an identity separate and distinct from others. Their lives have a nice balance; they are connected with people, not enmeshed with them. Imagine a picket fence with a gate: you get to decide who you want to come into your life and how far they come in. For instance, you may want to crack open the gate by limiting someone to a ten-minute phone call instead of inviting her or him over to your house. There may be a family member you want to honor, but his or her behavior may be so toxic that you must limit the relationship to a birthday card. Boundaries are flexible, so they can change. The most important thing to understand is that you are the gatekeeper controlling your life and space.

BOUNDARIES MAKE OTHERS FEEL SAFE

I used to think that people who had clear boundaries were mean and nasty and that people who accommodated everybody else's whim were "Christian." But I've come to admire people with clear-cut boundaries because there are no mixed messages, no mind games, and no guessing involved.

When my kids were small, I telephoned my friend Sue to see if she could watch them while I went to an appointment. She sighed deeply and mumbled, "Well . . . I guess . . ."

I took my children to her house but worried about them the entire time I was gone. I could tell she hadn't really wanted extra children that day, but like me, Sue was a pleaser who couldn't say no. Her inability to set strong, clear boundaries had the effect of making me feel oddly unsafe and uncomfortable.

Juxtapose that incident with another. Whenever I asked a favorite teacher if I could stop by for a visit, he clearly stated yes or no, with little explanation. I always felt safe asking, because I knew he wouldn't see me just because I wanted to visit. He knew how to protect his time. His ability to set concise, clear boundaries made me feel comfortable enough to ask things of him. Of course, it helps to state boundaries with a kind tone of voice; there's rarely a need to be harsh or rude.

HEALTHY BOUNDARIES ALLOW CLOSE RELATIONSHIPS

People with healthy boundaries are able to identify what they think and feel about something; those with unhealthy boundaries often allow others to tell them what they think or feel. People with healthy boundaries are able to control how they react, and they are able to distinguish between their own emotions, opinions, and behaviors and those of others. They take responsibility for how they think, feel, or behave, and do not blame others. They are very clear about where they end and another person begins, and they maintain that line. They are able to stand up for themselves calmly and intelligently without desperation, intimidation, or manipulation.

Individuals in a relationship need a clear sense of who they are in order to clearly communicate their needs to their partner. You can't do this if you are carrying someone else's emotions, blaming others for your behavior, or practicing someone else's beliefs. It may take years to develop an assertive healthy self. As we explored in the last chapter, some people go to their grave never having a sense of who they are. If this hits close to home, and you don't find healing through this book or through others or by talking with wise friends, invest in yourself by seeing a good counselor and talking about identity issues.

Healthy boundaries are not selfish. They allow us to feel genuine empathy for others, without taking responsibility for them. Because I am by nature a tenderhearted woman, when I decided to become a counselor my biggest fear was that I would take home other people's pain and problems. Surprisingly, and thankfully, this has not been the case—but I had learned the lesson of what was my responsibility and what was not. I am able to deeply empathize with a client in pain, without feeling the urge to own or fix it.

People with unhealthy boundaries find themselves "carrying" the feelings, ideas, or behavior of someone else. What's the cure? When you feel overwhelmed or overloaded, get renewed by taking a break, practice some of the self-care ideas in this book, and then ask what you can realistically do to help someone you love without owning their problems. Friends can be great resources for helping you see when you are showing healthy care for someone you love rather than allowing yourself to be overburdened, manipulated, or pulled into fixer mode.

ABLE TO HEAR *NO*

A healthy person is able to hear the word *no* from others without having his or her self-esteem shattered. Even if your needs are real, if someone says no, that's a boundary to be respected.

God made us to be relational, so it is inevitable that our families, coworkers, and friends will affect us. But a person with healthy boundaries will not allow himself or herself to base his or her sense of self-worth on the opinions or behaviors of others.

A healthy person will state her or his needs, and if those needs aren't respected, she or he will have consequences (such as distance) until the relationship gets repaired.

A healthy person avoids manipulation, guilt, bullying, or blame. She or he does not play the victim or the martyr, and she or he does not tolerate abuse.

Having healthy boundaries makes the resolution of problems much simpler and clearer. If someone hurts you, having healthy boundaries allows you to experience the hurt, understand you have a right to protest the hurt, and stand up for yourself. You can do this without placing guilt or blaming, but by simply stating that you are feeling hurt and asking that the behavior not be repeated. If the person who caused the hurt decides to keep hurting you, healthy boundaries will allow you to walk away. People with healthy boundaries do not allow themselves to be continually mistreated or abused.

HEALTHY BOUNDARIES

Some indications of people with healthy boundaries are:

- Ability to adapt and change when it is needed and appropriate
- Ability to avoid wild vacillation according to what is happening around them

- Able to say no when it is appropriate
- Able to accept constructive criticism or feedback without personalizing it
- Able to accept no from others without taking it personally
- Able to stand up for themselves
- Ability to understand how they feel, what they think, and how they behave
- Ability to take responsibility for getting needs met
- Ability to takes responsibility for their own emotions, ideas, and behavior

ARE BOUNDARIES BIBLICAL?

Maybe you think boundaries are confusing and contradictory—maybe even unbiblical. In the Letter to the Galatians 6:2 we read, "Carry each other's burdens, and in this way you will fulfill the law of Christ." A few verses later it says that each is responsible for his or her own load (6:5). I love the fact that Drs. Cloud and Townsend in their book *Boundaries* make a distinction between the biblical words *load* and *burden*. There is a big difference between the two. It is true that sometimes people are given a burden they cannot carry, and of course we will want to step in and help, probably along with a supportive "village" of other caring people. An example of this type of burden would be a job loss or a major health issue. But the Bible tells each person to carry his or her own load. An example of someone not carrying her own load might be the person who freeloads off her friends and refuses to get a job. Boundary problems come when someone tries to pass off his or her *load* as a *burden* for others to carry. Let's say you have a friend who comes to borrow money but continues to be irresponsible with his life. He is trying to make you carry his load. Now, let's say another friend's house burns down and you offer her a temporary place to live and regroup. That is carrying another's burden.

Some people may be good at setting boundaries with certain people but not with others. A young woman might be able to set healthy parameters with her boss but not with her neighbor. A father may give plenty of time to his children but forget to prioritize his wife. Christians, especially, struggle over the idea of setting boundaries, because they feel it would be unchristian to say no. But learning to set limits is a big part of self-care. Unless we can say no, we may be saying yes to everything except the people and projects to which God really wants us to devote our energy.

Let me give an example. Jeanette and Joe felt pressure from the pastor to take in some adult exchange students who would be interning at the church all summer. They did not feel comfortable saying no. All summer long they resented having to prepare meals for their guests. They couldn't take any of the motorcycle trips they had planned, which would have given them much-needed time to focus on their marriage. They grew agitated that they couldn't visit their grandchildren or offer relatives a place to stay during a family reunion. They did provide a place for the interns, but at what cost to their own stress level, marriage happiness, and time with family members? Of course there must be a balance between saying yes and saying no. Boundaries can certainly be taken to an extreme and used as an excuse to never serve others.

Many children are raised in an environment where they learn to set boundaries backward: they keep things inside that they shouldn't (for example, negative feelings and emotions about toxic people), and they assume that they have to accept what is not theirs (for example, the to-do lists and opinions of others). They don't give themselves permission to set limits with people, nor do they know how.

RIGID BOUNDARIES

Thus far we've talked about people with no boundaries or boundaries that are too permeable. However, at the other end of the spectrum are people with very rigid or closed boundaries who don't let anything in and rarely notice the effect of their behavior, opinions, or feelings on others. They may appear intrusive and perhaps even manipulative. They are masterful at blaming the victim for the resulting outcome. People with rigid boundaries tend to be withdrawn and to isolate themselves in relationships. Some indications of people with rigid boundaries are:

- Inflexibility
- Impervious or nonresponsive to feedback
- Inability to change; hanging on to how things "have always been done"
- Seeking stability at the price of flexibility
- Listening without responding or changing

- Impervious to anything outside of themselves or their own feelings

There are many varieties of boundary problems. See if any of these feel familiar.

ENMESHMENT

Cindy and Jack came to me because they were depressed. Three years into their marriage they couldn't understand where the love had gone and why the depression had entered. As I explored their relationship, I found that they did all of their activities together. When Jack wanted to have a night out once or twice a month to talk to his buddy, Cindy said it was inappropriate for him to be gone that much. Because Jack hadn't witnessed healthy boundaries in his home, he didn't know how to stand up for his needs. While the couple viewed their marriage as being extremely intimate, I observed it as unhealthy. Couples need time apart in order to gain a sense of identity outside the marriage. They need to have time away from each other in order to miss each other. I assigned them the task of doing things alone or with friends but not with each other. Eventually, their marriage started to improve.

Sometimes I draw Venn diagram circles for my clients to show them what a healthy relationship looks like. If you imagine two concentric circles, part of both should overlap; but they should not overlap completely (when they do, counselors call that "enmeshment"). Nor should they be so far apart that they don't touch. Successful marriage partners feel safe enough asking, from a vulnerable space, for their needs to be met. I discuss this in a later chapter about connection.

INABILITY TO OWN YOUR OWN BAGGAGE

The most common problem I see in marriage counseling is that two broken, unhealthy, unstable people get together hoping the one will fix the other. I picture two people exchanging suitcases full of childhood baggage. Wounds are multiplied in marriage and often don't reveal themselves clearly except within the context of a close relationship. The only way a marriage works well is for two relatively whole people to show up. Being whole means you have a sense of self (ego strength), and you don't get your identity by feeding off or being engulfed by your partner.

Unhealthy boundaries are often seen in relationships that are abusive. One partner will walk on eggshells around the other to avoid making the other mad or violent. The abused partner hides his or her emotions, opinions, and behaviors. If you are not allowed to have your own emotions, opinions, or behaviors in a relationship, this is emotional abuse. So many times when I see this dysfunctional pattern the partner being abused will justify it by saying, "But he never hits me, so it can't be abuse."

MIND GAMES

Barbara phoned her friend Alice. "You need to stop by and get the cookbook you loaned me." Though Barbara said it was about a cookbook, Alice had the impression that Barbara really wanted her to come see her granddaughter. Alice felt herself resisting and feeling manipulated. She wanted Barbara to ask for what she wanted directly (for example, "Can you come over? I'd really like for you to meet my grand-daughter"). Healthy people are able to recognize their needs and take responsibility for them—they don't manipulate others, place guilt on them, or make people guess what they really want. There are no bully tactics or mind games.

There are three basic ways that people put forth their needs in the world: *passively*, *assertively*, and *aggressively*. *Passive* people don't state clearly what their needs and desires are. Instead, they tend to go along with the wishes of others. In the long run, they end up not getting their needs met and become resentful.

Assertive people clearly state their wants and desires. It doesn't mean they always get their way, but others know where they stand. If two friends are going out to dinner and one suggests a restaurant that the other doesn't like, the other might say, "You know, I'm not crazy about Mexican food. Is there some other spot we both like?"

Aggressive people assert their will to get what they want. For example, instead of considering other people's opinions, an aggressive person would say, "Next year we're having the family reunion at the park by my house." Some people are openly aggressive ("My way or the highway"), and some are passive-aggressive—in other words, they get back at other people in an underhanded way instead of clearly stating their feelings. An example would be the wife who tells her husband, "No honey, I'm not mad," but then burns his toast on purpose.

Consider all the possible combinations within a relationship. Maybe one partner is passive and one is assertive. Or both are aggressive. I have observed that until both people learn to be assertive in healthy ways, without being passive, aggressive, or passive-aggressive, there can be no real intimacy or solid emotional connection. Learning how to be assertive is a great example of self-care.

SEXUAL ABUSE

Many people can't acknowledge how rampant sexual abuse is. In the United States at least one in three women, and one in six men, have been sexually abused before the age of eighteen. I would be remiss not to address this topic since it is such a common way for boundaries to be obliterated.

First of all, many adults have not consciously connected current symptoms with historic events. Jenny struggled with shame, fear of intimacy, anxiety, low-level depression, impulse control, explosive anger, alcohol abuse, and infrequent suicidal thoughts. She assumed this was just her temperament. "Depression runs in our family," she told her counselor. When the therapist asked if she had ever been sexually abused, she replied, "No way. Well, except there was the time my older cousin locked me in his pickup truck and touched me all over."

Most people don't understand the various forms sexual abuse takes: being touched in a way that feels uncomfortable; being shown sexual movies; being asked to pose for seductive photographs; being forced to perform oral sex on another; being bathed in a way that feels intrusive; being encouraged or goaded into sex that wasn't really wanted— all these are forms of abuse. Most people think that sexual abuse is rape by a stranger. Nothing could be further from the truth. Almost all sexual abuse comes from someone the victim loves and trusts, such as a brother, coach, teacher, or relative. Because the abuse came from someone the victim loves and trusts, and because she or he may have enjoyed gifts or feelings of specialness or even arousal, she or he becomes a colluder in her or his own abuse. The confusing result is that then the victim turns negative emotions on herself or himself for colluding.

Sometimes Christians are quick to expect victims to heal in a hurry. Victims are preached at, given pat answers, and expected to forgive and forget. But just as Nehemiah had to acknowledge the extent of the damage before he could begin repairing the walls around Jerusalem, survivors need to take many long steps before they heal.

Survivors must become fully aware of what happened. Then they have to break the silence and tell someone safe. It is important for them to tell their story in detail, understanding and gaining insight into their behaviors and emotions. In a way that is carefully paced, they need to work through their feelings with another safe person, perhaps a trained counselor or a support group. They need to learn self-care and symptom management as they tell their story. Then they finally can learn to forgive themselves and others and recreate a better story for themselves. This process can take months or years. Everyone navigates his or her own journey to healing, and the timeline is unique.

TOXIC PERSONALITIES

Recently, I experienced a frustrating situation where a friend falsely accused me. In letter after letter I tried to explain and defend myself. However, because she was so hurt, she convinced herself that I had betrayed her. She began telling lies about me. Since I am a pleaser, I thought the more I tried to argue my side, the more likely it would be that I would win her over and convince her of the truth.

Finally, a few of my friends asked me why I continued to put myself in the position of being hurt by her. "She's toxic," they told me. One of these friends asked, "Why do you keep going into a room with a wounded tiger? It's only going to leave you bloody." That visual image of a wounded tiger, and my continually volunteering for the "job," finally stopped the madness. Even though I stayed in this sick situation for far too long, I finally found a healthier way to respond to the situation. I told the person who was hurting me, and the others she was pulling in, that I felt hurt. Then I stepped away and moved toward friends who were kind and loving. Realizing that I was pouring time, words, and emotional effort down a black hole, I had to let go and allow God to be my defender. But I also had to run to real people who could give me perspective and who could comfort me.

Sometimes both people involved have boundary problems. I was at the post office and observed a man in line talking incessantly about politics to the woman next to him until it was his turn at the counter. Everyone assumed the man and woman were together. When it was his turn to be waited on, his back now to the line, the woman turned to the line of people and expressed a huge sigh of relief, and everyone laughed. But I saw a situation of unprotected boundaries. A person with healthy boundaries is able to say when her or his boundaries are being intruded upon. The woman could have easily told the man, "Well that's your opinion and I would rather not have this discussion." Instead she allowed herself to be his captive audience, even though it became clear later that she did not wish to be.

TIPS FOR SETTING BOUNDARIES

If you struggle with establishing healthy boundaries, here are some starting points for establishing renewal:

- Read *Boundaries* by Henry Cloud and John Townsend.
- Practice boundaries with strangers and people who you meet every day and who you are less invested in establishing boundaries with (for example, phone solicitors, door-to-door salespeople, restaurant servers).
- Practice saying no without reasons. Your reasons actually weaken your no and are usually apparent to others.
- Think of yourself in the third person (for example, "Lucille gets cranky when she's overwhelmed. This would not be good.").
- Realize that not setting boundaries is really about immaturity and about trying to get love from others in an unhealthy way. If people stop loving us because we set a healthy boundary, then they are toxic to us.
- Understand that taking time for yourself will help create a more harmonious environment for others. And you

won't present yourself to the world in an angry, resentful, and frustrated way.

Our spiritual lives form the core of our understanding of ourselves, affecting our boundaries and every part of our lives. In the next chapter, we will look at how renewing a focus on spirituality provides a means of self-care.

CHAPTER 4

RENEWED THROUGH SPIRITUAL SELF-CARE

*The spiritual life is a life in which you
gradually learn to listen to a voice that
says, "You are the beloved and on you my
favor rests." It is not a very loud voice
because it is an intimate voice.*

— HENRI NOUWEN

I FELT GIDDY AND EXCITED as I heard the
announcement at church that Sunday morning.
Our congregation was organizing a trip to Israel
and, although I had no idea how we could afford such a trip,
I told my husband that I wanted to go.

We were a single-income family with two young children
and bills to pay. I felt boxed in. Even if a "miracle check"

arrived in our mailbox, the money would surely be spent on more appropriate things. Yet I continued to pray and hope.

A few weeks later, I read this passage from the prophet Ezekiel: "This is what the Sovereign LORD says: Once again I will yield to the plea of the house of Israel and do this for them" (36:37). I immediately sensed that this was a personal message for me. I continued reading, and felt God telling me that my prayers would be answered. I would be going to Israel—for his name's sake. I penciled "January 14, 1999" along with the word "Israel" next to the passage in my Bible.

Although most of my fellow church members were aware that I didn't have the money to pay for the trip, I couldn't hide my excitement whenever the subject came up. When people asked if I would be going, I responded, "I hope to."

But as the weeks and months flew by, it did not look like I would be going to the Middle East. The itinerary was set and all those who would be traveling received their tickets. Sadly, my name was not on the roster. As ridiculous as it seemed, I couldn't shake the sense that I was supposed to be on that plane.

Then it happened. Three days before the scheduled trip, I received a call from my pastor. He said, "Lucille, someone paid for your trip. You are going to Israel!" Even he was incredulous. He said that someone bought my ticket but he was not allowed to reveal the donor's identity. I hung up the phone and sobbed. To this day I don't know who paid for that ticket.

Three days into our stay, we awoke early in the morning and made our way to the Mount of Beatitudes, which over-looks the Sea of Galilee. The air was foggy, dew dripped on the flowers and trees, and the shrill chirp of birds danced through the air. As we sat down in a huddle on the steps of the old church that had been built in that location I could picture Jesus walking with and talking to his followers.

Our Israeli guide began reading from Ezekiel 36. He began talking about the fact that God answers our prayers for "the sake of [God's] holy name" (v. 22), not for ours. My eyes pooled with tears as God once again confirmed the words I'd read months earlier. I was sitting on the steps of that church so that others would know who God is. God had answered my plea and provided the trip.

Rarely do life events happen so powerfully or so mystically. But they do happen. I am convinced that most people have at least one life event that caused them to ponder spiritual events.

SPIRITUALITY AND WELL-BEING

Being spiritual is not about self-sacrifice. It's about self-care and paying attention to your inner pilot light. If you've ever made a quiet time part of your daily practice, you probably know how off-kilter you feel when you miss it. When you make time for spiritual self-care you learn to listen to your own voice as well as God's, and most often you find peace.

Lissa Rankin is a medical doctor who burned out trying to address what helped and what hindered her patients. She would treat one symptom in her patients only to have another pop up. After several catastrophic events happened to Dr. Rankin herself in a very short time, she poured herself into researching what really helped people stay healthy. You

can listen to what she says in this TED talk: http://www.you
tube.com/watch?v=7tu9nJmr4Xs.

She concluded that the body doesn't shape how we live
our lives but is instead a mirror of how we live our lives. Yes,
eating healthy, getting plenty of sleep, and exercising contribute to a person's physical health. But Dr. Rankin was
stunned by the research (not always found in medical jour-
nals) that made the biggest difference. She discovered physical health is most affected by the following factors:

- A person's relationships
- Quality of one's professional life
- Ability to express one's self creatively
- Having a healthy sex life
- Having a secure financial state
- Being in a healthy environment
- Being mentally healthy
- Being spiritually connected

Spirituality signifies the inner attitude of living life in
search of the sacred, a search for meaning in life through
something more powerful and bigger than ourselves. It is the
way we invite God into our daily lives. One philosopher and
writer calls it "the wild joy we humans fall into." Another
writer, Elizabeth Harper Neeld, says, "The spiritual life is the
core of who we are. It is Life with a capital L. It is that part of
us that knows infinity. That loves. That longs for connection.
That is unsatisfied without purpose and meaning. That is
moved by ritual. That is timeless" (A Sacred Primer, 20).

The sacred—the spiritual—comes in many forms. Growing evidence confirms the link between well-being and spirituality. Abraham Maslow, an American psychologist best known for creating the hierarchy of needs, called these "peak experiences." Others call it ecstasy, serendipity, compassion, hope, gratitude, love, and awe. But ultimately what we are talking about are those moments of highest happiness—a state of well-being where one is calm and aware of being satisfied with life. People who experience these peaks have greater feelings of self-confidence and a deeper sense of meaning and purpose. Health researchers are even including spirituality as an important component in programs for reversing heart disease.

Spirituality can help people develop happiness and satisfaction with life, as well as prevent the stresses and lifestyle that lead to physical and mental disorders. In fact, religious people report being happier and more satisfied with life than nonreligious people. For instance, 47 percent of people who report attending religious services several times a week describe themselves as "very happy," versus 28 percent who attend less than once a month. Spirituality may have positive effects on people because it is connected with marital status, healthy behaviors and activities, social support, optimism, hope, purpose, sense of identity, and internal locus of control.

A study that examined people who have suffered traumatic life events found that those who had a strong religious faith fared better psychologically than those who did not have a strong faith, perhaps because they trusted that everything has a purpose. In fact, spirituality is so powerful that during hard times it is the single most frequently used form of coping by older people.

SPIRITUALITY IS NOT ALWAYS JOYFUL

Yet, having a deep spirituality is not always joyful. Many people have experienced a close connection with God during their darkest days. I think back to several of my own experiences. When I suffered a severe dog bite and subsequent phobia, I quit the one hobby I loved above all others: running. Unaware that phobias, including agoraphobia, become self-perpetuating, the number of places where I felt safe dwindled. I began seeing a counselor who specialized in phobias, because I was anxious and depressed. During the long drive across town, listening to Rich Mullins's songs comforted me in a way that was indescribable. Never had I felt closer to God.

Then one day, the most random thing happened. A police officer in Waterloo, Iowa, e-mailed me because he saw my comments on a website about Rich Mullins. It turns out that he and Rich were close friends before Rich's fatal Jeep accident. He sent several snapshots of himself and Rich, and made cassette tapes of some of Rich's favorite Irish music. He even offered to mail them to my church if I didn't feel safe giving him my address.

I remember where I was and the sensation I had watching sunshine on the snow when I realized God loved me so much to encourage me in this specific way. Elizabeth Harper Neeld says, "Sacred experience comes in many forms. It can be as quiet as a walk in a garden or as comforting as a cup of tea at the kitchen table." Eventually our families became friends, and we visited them in Iowa. Exposure to their German shepherd Champ eradicated my phobia of dogs.

Maybe God really does go out of the way to comfort us with the Holy Spirit, or maybe our vulnerability increases our sensitivity and receptivity to a God who is always speaking to us. I live in the community where the Columbine High School tragedy occurred in 1999. Forty-nine of the students belonged to our church, including one who was killed. For months, the local churches overflowed with people. I remember typically sedate worshipers spontaneously coming to their feet, thrusting hands upward, and belting out the lyrics to songs as we all tried to heal. Everyone seemed to sense the power of the Holy Spirit. The same things happened after the 9/11 attacks. My husband and I were stranded in a fancy hotel in Miami where we witnessed the bar lounge turn into a church. The televisions in the lounge showed our country's leaders gathered for a prayer service. A crowd began to form around me. Grown men were weeping, joining in the worship service and singing "The Battle Hymn of the Republic."

WHAT SPIRITUAL EXPERIENCES LOOK LIKE

Spiritual experiences show up as a coincidence, conversion, near-death experience, awakening, mystery, energy, emotion, beauty, awe, wonder, and silence. These experiences show up in ways that cannot be put into words, and they don't have to be earth-shattering. Sometimes the best moments are when we hear the still, small voice of God.

Mother Teresa said, "We need to find God, and [God] cannot be found in noise and restlessness. . . . The more we receive in silent prayer, the more we can give in our active life. We need silence to touch souls" (*A Gift for God*, 68–69). In order to do that, we must carve a time, space, and frame of mind, free of distraction, to nurture our spirituality.

CREATING SPACE AND PLACE FOR SPIRITUALITY

You can cultivate a spiritual time for yourself in various ways: meditation, reading, listening to music, making a meal, creating art, and pursuing quiet. Years ago, I believed that a prayer time had to be done with certain requirements, such as a thirty-minute Bible study. Now, I'm not so rigid. I have a basket in my living room filled with an assortment of items: lavender lotion, candles, four or five books (some are devotionals and some are not), iPod and headphones, a notepad where I jot down things I'm thankful for, and colorful pencils. Some days, I read one verse and meditate on it as I watch the snow hang from the tree in my front yard. Other days I read from all five books and my Bible as well. I don't beat myself up if I miss a day of reading my Bible. Sometimes I don't even make it to my "quiet spot." Instead, I lie in bed for twenty to thirty minutes in a half-awake, half-asleep state and pray for everyone I can think of. And every day, I talk to God all day long. Teresa of Avila said, "The life of prayer is just the love of God and liking to be with him."

WHEN GOD SEEMS HIDDEN

Many of us act as if we believe God to be a cosmic soda machine. We put our prayers in and we hope something good rolls out. But that is a sign of an immature faith. A more mature faith trusts that God has our good at heart even when we don't get our wishes. Sometimes we do get what we pray for. Sometimes we do not. Sometimes God simply surprises us with blessings beyond our ability to hope for or ask for. And sometimes, like Garth Brooks's song says, we "thank God for unanswered prayers." Sometimes the outcome happens over time; sometimes the answer is better than we could have ever hoped; and sometimes the answer never comes but we experience emotional and spiritual growth through the process of waiting.

The Bible shows us that prayer changes things: Jacob wrestled with God and prevailed (Genesis 32), sickly Hezekiah prayed and lived fifteen more years (Isaiah 38:2-8), and evil King Manasseh cried out from captivity and was rescued (2 Chronicles 33:11-13). The prayers of a righteous person avail much (James 5:15). I like to think that the process of prayer is much more important than the outcome.

In my counseling practice I always pray before each session. Whatever happens in that room, I know I prepared myself to rely on the Holy Spirit. Without prayer, my counseling practice would be limited to my own thoughts and education.

SPIRITUAL PRACTICES CONNECT US TO
OURSELVES AND OTHERS

Spirituality doesn't only put us in touch with God; it also
puts us in touch with ourselves. Musician and professor John
Dunne says, "By remembering love, by remembering God,
. . . then I begin to know myself, to know my heart." Routinely when I am hiking, gardening, practicing yoga, jogging,
or cooking, I am reflecting on life and opening myself up to
it. I am thinking about my interactions in the world, hopefully
considering what sort of legacy I want to leave and what I
can do for others.

The monastic writer Brother Lawrence is famous for teaching us that cooking and dishwashing can be times for practicing the presence of God. When I asked my friends about
their favorite ways to connect with God, several said,
"through nature," for example, experiencing sunrises or
thunderstorms when alone or hiking a trail and taking pho-
tos. Another sensed it when she was in the presence of a
family she never thought she would have. One friend realized that when she feels close to God, she makes sure she
has cash on hand. She is amazed at how many times God
reveals to whom she should give the money.

Mindfulness, deep breathing, and meditation are renewing, powerful forms of self-care, yet these words may be
scary—some people fear the link to Eastern mysticism. But
the Bible teaches about godly meditation practice. Mindfulness is the opposite of multitasking. Being able to stay in the
present moment is routinely linked with happiness levels.
Being mindful about the way you live facilitates sleep and

wakefulness. I notice that when I see clients after my yoga class, I feel more present and more relaxed about whatever will be presented to me. Here's what Christian author Rachel Held Evans says about mindfulness:

> When I practice mindfulness in conversation, I listen to what others are saying rather than worrying about what I'm going to say next.
>
> When I practice mindfulness in eating, I savor and enjoy smaller portions instead of absently scarfing down an entire can of Pringles while watching "The Biggest Loser." . . .
>
> When I practice mindfulness while reading Scripture, I am more in tune with how the Holy Spirit is speaking to me at that moment and less concerned about which theological system best explains what I've read.
>
> When I practice mindfulness while praying, I find myself doubting less and believing more. ("A Little Mindfulness Never Hurt Anyone")

For some religious traditions, such as Buddhism, meditation is a practice of trying to empty the mind by concentrating on one's breath. But I prefer "centering prayer" as a form of Christian meditation. In this practice, I contemplate a spiritual truth and become fully present in the moment. That truth could be something as simple as, "The Lord is my Shepherd," or, "I am a new creature in Christ," or, "There is no fear in love." And I just let that truth sink deeply into my brain, heart, and soul.

New research shows meditation contributes to brain health. It has been shown to help a variety of health problems, including quitting smoking, coping with cancer, and even preventing psoriasis. Countless studies show that meditation reduces stress, although much of the research has focused on high blood pressure and heart disease. Meditation may also help you be more mindful of food choices. With practice, a person may be able to pay better attention to the impulse to grab a fat- and sugar-loaded comfort food and inhibit the impulse.

The Bible is filled with examples of encouragement to be mindful and meditative (emphasis added):

> Finally, brothers [and sisters], whatever is true, whatever is noble, whatever is right, whatever is pure, whatever is lovely, whatever is admirable—if anything is excellent or praiseworthy—*think about such things.* (Philippians 4: 8)

> Then he went down to Nazareth with them and was obedient to them. But his mother *treasured all these things in her heart.* (Luke 2:51)

> This is what the LORD says to me:
> "I will remain quiet and will look on from my dwelling place,
> like shimmering heat in the sunshine,
> like a cloud of dew in the heat of harvest." (Isaiah 18:4)

> After the wind there was an earthquake, but the LORD was not in the earthquake. After the earthquake came a fire, but the LORD was not in the fire. And after the fire came *a gentle whisper.* (1 Kings 19:11-12)

WAYS TO INTEGRATE SPIRITUALITY FOR RENEWAL AND SELF-CARE

- Author Wayne Muller says spiritual acts "need not be showy or dramatic, for the most potent spiritual acts are often acts of breathtaking simplicity: a simple prayer, a sip of wine and a piece of bread, a single breath in meditation, a sprinkle of water on the forehead, an exchange of rings, a kind word, a hand on a cheek, a blessing." (*How, Then, Shall We Live?*, 207)

- Light a candle as a way to delineate the time and space.
- Consider these questions: Who are the people who mean the most to me? If I knew I had one month to live, what would be on my "bucket list"? With whom do I need to make peace? One of my best memories is . . .
- Sing a praise song or strum a guitar.
- Type out a prayer or psalm and hang it on your refrigerator. Stop and read it often.
- Play a song on your iPod, close your eyes, and listen to the words.
- Speak a phrase of truth. One I particularly love is, "A gentle healer came into our town today." And then I visualize Jesus walking a dusty path, helping and healing.
- Be silent. Ask God to speak to you. Focus on one word, such as *joy, love, mercy, hope*, and so on. Quiet, sacred time does not just happen. It must be intentionally created.
- Scatter a few encouraging books around your house. My bathroom has several inspirational books, and my kitchen table has a small flip calendar with Scripture.
- Pray for one person, and let that person know that you prayed.
- Scan your memory for inexplicable life events. Can they be attributable to God, or are they just circumstance?

- Consider taking a yoga class. Yoga is simply stretching, balancing, and breathing. If you take it at a recreation center, there is less chance it will be focused on Eastern religion.
- Keep a journal of your thoughts.
- Inhale to a count of five, hold for a count of five, and then breathe out for a count of five. Deep breathing has a calming, centering effect. It supplies your blood with oxygen and dispels carbon dioxide. Imagine you are breathing in joy and breathing out anxiety.
- As you eat or drink, take a mental snapshot. Savor the moment.
- Read some Scripture, even out loud. Read a devotional. Some of my favorites are written by Ken Gire, Frederick Buechner, Brennan Manning, Henri Nouwen, Patricia Raybon, and Lael Arrington.
- Spend time in nature. Walk; think; let your mind relax.
- Take a hike, alone. Rest near a quiet stream. Sit on a majestic overlook. Talk to God.
- Go to a farm, nursery, or botanical garden and take photographs.
- Think about a time when you were connected to something greater than yourself.

One aspect of attending to our spiritual lives is understanding the renewing value of solitude. In the next chapter, we will focus on solitude as a means of self-care.

CHAPTER 5

RENEWED THROUGH SOLITUDE

Let him who cannot be alone beware of community. Let him who is not in community beware of being alone.

—DIETRICH BONHOEFFER

PROFESSOR WILLIAM DERESIEWICZ tells the incoming students at the United States Military Academy at West Point, "If you want others to follow, learn to be alone with your thoughts." Though it sounds like a contradiction because we imagine leaders surrounding themselves with people, Deresiewicz tells the future leaders that solitude will be the thing they have the least of, yet it is the most necessary ingredient for true leadership.

Someone who stands out as a leader who has learned to be alone with his thoughts is General David Petraeus, a military man who rose through the bureaucracy by being an intellectual. Because he had the capacity to think for himself, due to the fact that he spent a lot of time alone, he had the courage to argue his ideas even when they weren't popular.

SOLITUDE IS SPARSE IN OUR CULTURE

Solitude is the time when we disengage from the immediate demands of other people, experience a reduction of social inhibition, and select our own activities, including creative thinking or prayer. For most people, solitude is sparse—so sparse that silence is a powerful means of capturing our attention. Silence is so powerful that when certain commercials use it, we perk up. Our world is radically changing into noisy interruptions and sound bites that are rewiring our brains.

Many of us spend hours on computers, interacting with others all day long. Some estimate that 30 to 40 percent of people's time in the workplace is spent tending to unplanned interruptions and then trying to refocus. Because technology is taking away our ability to be alone, we have less and less time to think and feel. Instead of marinating in our own thoughts long enough to have an idea, we bombard our brains with the thoughts of others—and those around us powerfully influence our decisions.

How can people be creative when they can't find space

and time to think? Thinking means concentrating on one thing long enough to develop your own idea about it. Only by concentrating, focusing, and being patient do we arrive at an original idea. Concentration can't happen between the TV, magazine, satellite radio, iPod, e-mail, Facebook, Twitter, and YouTube. Right now, I am trying to write a simple sentence about the decline of creativity in the United States. In trying to convey a point about solitude and its importance to creativity, I can't think because I'm staring at my to-do list and e-mails that pop onto on my computer screen. And my phone just started ringing.

Recently one of my son's friends, a freshman at a university, invited me to sit in on his psychology course. It had been two and a half decades since I had been a student in the very same auditorium, and a lot had changed. As the chairs filled up, almost every student flipped open a laptop, and there was a steady barrage of talking. I anticipated that the room would quiet down and the students would begin taking notes on their computers. Wrong! Instead I saw video games, sports cars racing across screens, and Facebook pages. About halfway through the class, the laptops were folded shut and the students took notes in old-fashioned notebooks. The computers had simply been a means for them to connect with their peers at the same time they were attending class.

I couldn't believe how much the world had changed, and I was impressed at the students' ability to multitask. Yet shortly after that experience, I read about a study led by a team of researchers at Stanford University who wanted to understand how today's college students multitask so much more efficiently than older adults. What did the research conclude? The study found the more young people multi-tasked, the worse they performed on mental tasks. The "high multitaskers" were unable to distinguish between relevant and irrelevant information, and they were also more easily distracted.

WHY IS SOLITUDE SO HARD TO ATTAIN?

For many people the thought of experiencing solitude is frightening. It is a well-known fact that solitary confinement is one of the worst forms of punishment. No one wants to be lonely, isolated, or alienated. As a twin raised in a large family, I had never experienced aloneness. When I transferred to a different college from my sister, I felt scared and panicky, so I made sure I was always around others. Many years later I learned that there is the huge difference between loneliness and solitude. I love theologian Paul Tillich's explanation: "Loneliness is the pain of being alone and solitude is the glory of being alone."

Solitude gets a bad rap. It's not polite to say, "I don't want to spend time with people today. I'd rather be alone." Loners are seen as eccentric, defective, and lonely. It's interesting to note that despite the stereotype of the lonely old person, loneliness is not associated with age. Ironically, loneliness decreases with age. Loneliness is instead linked with illness, immobility, and being unmarried.

Christians often feel guilty taking time to be by themselves in a world that demands so much love and care. Author Wayne Muller writes: "Our reluctance to rest—our belief that our joy and delight may somehow steal from the poor, or add to the sorrows of those who suffer—is a dangerous and corrosive myth, because it creates the illusion that service to others is a painful and dreary thing" (*Sabbath*, 49). There is a time for every purpose under heaven, including time to rest and nourish ourselves with solitude. Once we experience rest, we have the emotional, physical, and spiritual capacity to truly love others.

Solitude doesn't have to mean introspection. It can mean sustained concentration on a particular topic, or it can mean creating a quiet space for thoughts to enter. There are two components of solitude: physical distance from others and mental disengagement. But counterintuitively, solitude can even happen within an intimate conversation between two friends. Deresiewicz says:

> Introspection means talking to yourself, and one of the best ways of talking to yourself is by talking to another person. One other person you can trust, one other person to whom you can unfold your soul. One other person you feel safe enough with to allow you to acknowledge things—to acknowledge things to yourself—that you otherwise can't. Doubts you aren't supposed to have, questions you aren't supposed to ask. Feelings or opinions that would get you laughed at by the group or reprimanded by the authorities. ("Solitude and Leadership")

BENEFITS OF SOLITUDE

So what do people gain from spending time in solitude? One researcher said the mere presence of other people obliges us to coordinate our actions. Right now I am alone. Snow is falling silently outside, and the only sound I hear comes from water trickling in my office fountain. Right now I can do whatever I want. I can slurp my split pea soup while taking intermittent bites of a chocolate bar. I can sit on my chair with one leg tucked under in unladylike fashion. I can take a break to let the dog out, and I can sing badly while doing all of the above. These little freedoms are not to be underestimated.

Humans may be social beings, but solitude has been shown to have great societal value. It is like the rests in a line of music, giving nuance and structure to the melody. Without it, our lives are a cacophony, a never-ending noise that wears us down. Solitude is essential for our spiritual experience—it is where we hear the still, small voice. Jesus was our model, showing us how to balance being with people and being alone: "Very early in the morning, while it was still dark, Jesus got up, left the house and went off to a solitary place, where he prayed" (Mark 1:35); "Jesus often withdrew to lonely places and prayed" (Luke 5:16). In these verses we see Jesus becoming known as a great healer and teacher, but he still took time to rest and pray.

I read about a reality show in England where regular people leave their hectic lives and join a monastery for ten weeks. They get to join monks who have no idea who is joining them, and they have an opportunity to incorporate deeply religious experiences into their lives. One of the contestants was a wealthy man who worked in the porn industry. This man's experience in the monastery was so profound that he left his job and joined the church. A deeply quiet and reflective life was obviously more appealing than a lucrative job in the sex industry.

Though God made us relational, solitude is what recharges

our batteries. Muller writes:

> Later, in the book of Exodus, we read, "In six days God made heaven and earth, and on the seventh day God rested, and was refreshed." Here, the word "refreshed," *vaiynafesh*, literally means, *and God exhaled*. The creation of the world was like the life-quickening inhale; the Sabbath is the exhale. . . . Without the Sabbath exhale, the life-giving inhale is impossible. (*Sabbath*, 36)

Inhale plus exhale equals life.

Being with people changes our experience. Consider how viewing a painting in a museum changes when another person walks nearby. Recently I went to see a movie that touched a deep place in my soul. In fact, I was close to tears for two days afterward, and I spent a solid night intermittently dreaming and thinking about it. It was a moment of serendipity that I chose to see this movie alone, and I imagine my entire experience would have been different had I been with another. I think I would have stayed on a cognitive and social plane, wondering what the other person thought of the movie and how we would discuss it later on, instead of letting the movie take me to an introspective and passionate place.

Solitude is where we turn our attention inwardly to find creative thought; creativity is what feeds our soul. In addition, solitude creates a ripe space for epiphanies. How often have you heard someone say that they had a great idea in the shower, on a morning run, or on a quiet ski slope? My clients' greatest ahas seem to happen when they express to themselves unacknowledged doubts, feelings, and opinions in my presence. Each of us is a creative person, whether we think we are or not. Some of the most brilliant heroes took time away for napping and thinking. These include Winston

Churchill, Napoleon Bonaparte, Thomas Edison, John Kennedy, and Ronald Reagan.

Most of us, however, have little down time. I've seen people race around with an inexhaustible need to be entertained and busy, scared of loneliness and the prospect of a silent house. People say they want stillness and rest, but when they have it, they immediately look for something to distract them. There is a brilliant video on YouTube that has more than five million hits: "How to Be Alone." In the video Andrea Dorfman and Tanya Davis address the fears and joys of being alone.

Happiness researcher Mihaly Csikszentmihalyi (pronounced, "chicks send me high") found that adolescents who cannot tolerate being alone often fail to develop their creative talents. When levels of outside stimulation drop, it seems people begin to generate sensations, daydreams, novel thoughts, and emotions.

Another benefit of alone time is experiencing creative changes in our self-concept. Whenever I go on a long road trip alone, I sing, cry, laugh, talk to myself, and think. And I think I grow emotionally. It feels like my true self blooms. That's because solitude separates us from the people and objects that define and confirm our identities. We often gain a new understanding of our priorities and ourselves.

When we are alone we are able to find intimacy with ourselves. The poet Lord Byron described solitude as the place where we are least alone, and Henry David Thoreau wrote, "I have a great deal of company in my house; especially in the morning, when nobody calls." Psychologists believe that it is our ability to securely attach to others, and to symbolically internalize a safe caregiver, that allows us to develop the capacity to be alone. In a strange twist of irony, people who haven't developed strong attachments to others may be the least likely to be able to handle being alone. It's paradoxical. As Philip Koch said, "We avoid loneliness by experiencing solitude against the backdrop of our social relations. . . . Loneliness can be kept at bay as long as we are aware in some way that we have meaningful connections to other people" (Long and Averill, "Solitude," 28).

Some people are never going to be comfortable spending time alone. Even if they are home alone, they occupy themselves with computers, TVs, and telephones. Research shows that people who are open to new emotional experiences, who are securely attached, and who are able to draw on inner resources instead of leaning on external supports such as routine, always being with people, and busyness are poised to benefit from solitude. People without these character traits will most likely feel anxious and try to distract themselves when they are alone. Muller writes:

> Our willingness to rest depends on what we believe we will find there. At rest, we come face-to-face with the essence of life. If we believe life is fundamentally good, we will seek out rest as a taste of goodness. If we believe life is fundamentally bad or flawed, we will be reluctant to quiet ourselves, afraid of meeting the darkness that resides in things—or in ourselves. (*Sabbath*, 40)

HOW TO PUT MORE SOLITUDE INTO YOUR LIFE

- When you're at home, agree to check social media for only five minutes on the hour.

- Spend time doing what you're good at, what you like to do, and what aligns with your values.
- Go someplace beautiful. If you're in the city, find a quiet museum or botanical garden.
- Find times to turn off cell phones altogether. For instance, I always leave my phone on mute when I am at home. When I get a break in my projects, I check my phone for voice messages.
- Grab a journal, a water bottle, and your Bible. Go to a quiet park and see what happens.
- Have slow, meaningful conversations with people.
- Before you are fully awake, let your thoughts meander. Talk to God. This is one of the few places and times you won't get distracted. Ask God to guide you about where you should spend your time and energy today.
- Read books that are thoughtful, lyrical, and beautiful.
- Say no to the things that drain you. Say yes to the things that give you life.
- Exercise in the outdoors rather than at a gym or on a home treadmill.
- Turn off the radio, TV, and phone.

In the next chapter, we turn our attention to sharing our secrets in safety, and how this can be a means of self-care.

CHAPTER 6

RENEWED THROUGH SHARING YOUR SECRETS

*To live by grace means to acknowledge
my whole life story, the light side and the
dark. In admitting my shadow side I learn
who I am and what God's grace means.*

—BRENNAN MANNING

I HEARD A STORY about one of my favorite
singers, the late Rich Mullins. He was in his mid-
forties and had just come from Amsterdam to a
train station in Germany. He had been talking to his best
friend Beaker in explicit detail about the nature of his temp-
tation and struggle against sin, when a stranger behind him
said, "Hey, aren't you Rich Mullins?" Rich wasn't sure if he

wanted the stranger to know who he was. He was ashamed that his secrets might have been overheard. As he retraced his conversation, he concluded, "I must be," whether he wanted to be or not.

I think most of us can relate to that story. How many of us wish for a different past? A clean slate? Or wish our minds never wandered to unhealthy places or that we were somehow mistake-proof human beings? How many of us have accepted the forgiveness Christ offers but still cannot forgive ourselves? Many of us are familiar with secret shame. The word secret comes from a French word that means "to sift apart." One of the primary reasons I wanted to write this book was because I experienced frustration and pain that sifted me apart, but also experienced the cure that put me back together. All people can throw off their shame by telling their secrets.

A DARK PATH

I have a past that I wish I didn't have. I was raised in a church that stressed that my good works would get me to heaven, but I knew that my bad deeds had taken on a life of their own. In spite of—or perhaps because of—this pressure, my behavior soon spiraled out of control. As a counselor, I now understand why I did what I did. I had a painful story and nowhere to tell it. I had intense confusion, boundary violations, and great loss, along with no healthy models for coping with the storm in my home. I tried reaching out to a teacher, but my ill mother felt threatened that the teacher and his wife were taking me away from the church of my upbringing. The life raft being offered drifted away. I turned to guys, drugs, and booze.

In college, my recklessness left me lonely and suicidal. In fact, one night I was on my dorm ledge, lonely and drunk. I wanted to change my lifestyle, but I struggled to find an alternative one. The girls in my dorm thought I was a wild child, so it was hard to fit in when I really needed a friend. I have very few memories of my freshman and sophomore years, but here's a smattering: dancing in the fountain at 2 a.m.; taking hallucinogens and crying in my bedroom; walking, with bare feet, in dirty snow on a freeway; overhearing a smart premed student say, "That Lucille, she's such a pretty girl, but what a waste"; and being sent to a counselor and fined $50 for having something on my ledge (myself!).

Even now, my memories of those two years haunt me. Somehow I survived and transferred from a small religious school to a giant school with a party reputation, but it was there that I turned off the severe self-destruct button. Even though I escaped the superdestructive lifestyle, it was decades before I could look in a mirror without dissociating and calling myself horrendous names.

It was only in my late thirties that I began to fall in love with myself; say kind things to myself; bestow grace, forgiveness, and acceptance on myself; and look wide-eyed at myself without shame.

SAFELY SHARING OUR SECRETS

The mind has an amazing capacity to ward off what is unpleasant, painful, or doesn't mesh with who we want to be. Many people get good at denying, minimizing, and distorting a painful past.

Secrets are like trash in a compacter. Over the years, we push more and more garbage down. We think our secrets stay hidden, but they rarely do. Our history leaks out like nuclear waste that eats holes in our soul. Our history reveals itself in the form of anger, guilt, addiction, anxiety, depression, eating disorders, and self-injury. The list is endless. When my clients share secrets, they usually fear that I'll react in shock or disgust. Instead I experience hurt and compassion for the pain that pulverizes people's lives, and I feel joy in their courage to talk openly. I feel privileged and honored to walk with them from shame to freedom.

It's important, though, to know that we are safe as we share our secrets—even with one trustworthy person. But some people are frightened and completely try to hide or contain their secrets. When a person compartmentalizes his or her life, as we too often see in well-known pastors or sports celebrities whose choices suddenly get exposed, the person is disintegrated (the opposite of integrity, when the outside of the apple matches the inside). The Swiss physician and author Dr. Paul Tournier gained worldwide fame in the 1960s helping people with their psychological and spiritual health. He said:

> We need to see that universal sickness, that innumerable throng of men and women laden down with their secrets, laden down with their fears, their sufferings, their sorrows, their disappointments, and their guilt. . . . Yet what eats away at them from within is that they may live years without finding anyone in whom they have enough confidence to unburden themselves. (*To Understand Each Other*, 49)

Research confirms Dr. Tournier's wisdom of unburdening: emotional disclosure is linked to reduced medical costs, less absenteeism at work, better immune functioning, better physical health, and increased psychological well-being. There is actual measurable evidence on the benefits of verbal emotional disclosure! For people who have suffered trauma without the release valve of talking through it, the trauma tends to stays bungled up—stuck—in their minds. And yet, the minute someone touches their psychological sunburn, they react.

But by talking, by releasing the secrets, the various parts of the brain that store the emotional memory integrate with the part that is able to put it into words. By writing and talking (and expressing the accompanying emotion), people are able to create a narrative, or story, of their experience—giving it a beginning, middle, and end. When people do this, they find closure. There is a fascinating book, *Opening Up*, written by psychologist and researcher James Pennebaker. His studies found that people spend much of their time thinking about something that is unresolved. He writes, "People have a basic need for completing and resolving tasks." Once understanding and resolution happens, it literally frees up space in our minds that we've been renting to rumination or fear (*Opening Up*, 90).

This step of renewal can be a startlingly difficult step. However, I recommend sharing your painful secrets to a select few safe people. I've made the mistake of prematurely sharing intimate events of my life with people who stared at me in silence; but eventually I used my "What is she telling me about herself?" question (as described in an earlier chapter) to understand that if people were uncomfortable with an honest story told in good faith, their discomfort probably had more to do with their own issues and was not a reflection on me.

So how do you decide with whom and how much you should share? Consider what Jesus did. He reserved his private thoughts for those he trusted the most: his disciples; and he shared most privately with Peter, John, and James. Start slowly. If you think someone might be safe, offer a little edge of your story and see what she or he does with it. If you receive a response that is judgmental, superior, or indifferent, stop sharing.

Safe people open the door for you to share more—at your own pace. They listen rather than telling you where you are. They are caring rather than offering trite answers or religious platitudes (for example, "Trust Jesus"). They invite. Rather than closing you down, they open you up. They are humble.

I don't believe God makes bad things happen to us, but I do believe God allows trials in our lives that will mold and shape us. Scripture says God will comfort us so that we can comfort others (2 Corinthians 1:4). But if we can't heal or even acknowledge our stories, how can our stories be useful and healing for others? Henri Nouwen said, "The main question is not 'How can we hide our wounds?' so we don't have to be embarrassed but 'How can we put our woundedness in the service of others?' When our wounds cease to be a source of shame and become a source of healing, we have become wounded healers" (*Bread for the Journey*, July 8).

For me, it wasn't the Bible or becoming a Christian that healed my shame. Those were pieces of my healing. For me, it was finding a place to be authentic in relationship with others that finally made my shame pack up bags and move out.

Look for places where you can be completely transparent—places where you don't have to be anyone other than who you are. Author Wayne Muller writes: "It is vital and true and deeply required that we tell our story. We must trace the shape of it, speak of the place in our body where it still lives, weep the tears of it, allow it to be seen and known. To have someone know the story of how we came here, how we came to be this way" (*How, Then, Shall We Live?* 35).

CREATING SAFE PLACES TO SHARE SECRETS

One of the great gifts we can offer others is the creation of a safe place for others to tell their stories. When I was learning to tell my story to a professor whom I hoped was trustworthy, and I needed a sense of being heard as well as anonymity, gracefully and instinctively the professor dimmed a light in his office so that it would be safe for me to tell my shameful story.

Will we offer grace instead of judgment? My professor did when I looked up and he said, "You think I love you less. I love you more for having the courage to tell it." Or are we more like Pharisees and religious rulers who drag people into the temple, ready to throw stones so we can feel somehow superior? Will we keep people's stories safe?

One of the most beautiful acts of compassion in the New Testament is the moment Jesus reached out to the woman caught in adultery—caught in the very act. She hadn't had time to shower or clean herself up. Jesus took the focus off of her by daring anyone in the surrounding crowd who was presumptuous enough to consider himself or herself sinless, to throw the first accusing stone. Then he bent down and began writing in the dirt. (Some people think he may have been writing down names of others in the crowd who had also sinned and had tried to hide it.) One by one the rocks dropped from humbled hands, and the accusers dispersed (John 7:53–8:11). The only one who can throw stones doesn't carry them.

Qualitative researcher Brené Brown spent ten years study-ing shame (you can watch her TED talk in Houston, "The Power of Vulnerability," on YouTube). One day as she was compiling all her research on shame and vulnerability (six year's worth of stories, interviews, and data), she came to a shattering conclusion that changed the way she lived, loved, and worked. She began thinking about connection and how it is the one thing that gives purpose and meaning to our lives. She began thinking of shame as being the fear of dis-connection ("Is there something about me that would make me unworthy of connection if other people knew about it or saw it?"). Unless you're a person who has no capacity for empathy or human connection, it is a universal feeling to wonder about being good enough, rich enough, or smart enough. She began to see that in order for connection to happen, there has to be excruciating vulnerability. We have to allow ourselves to be seen—really seen.

Years ago, I heard a woman call a talk show where coun-selors offered advice. The first thing she did was apologize for calling, because her life was nearly perfect. She had a great home and family; she was attractive and educated, and everyone around her was in good health. Nothing was really wrong except that she was lonely. The counselors asked her when she ever let people see her flaws, insecurities, and imperfections. When she admitted that she didn't, they told her other people couldn't relate to someone who acted per-fect. This was the reason no one wanted to spend time with her.

In contrast, I have a friend on Facebook who daily admits all the goofy things that happen in her life. Hundreds of friends respond to her because authenticity is what draws people in. It's a paradox: when we tell people about our fears, flaws, and failures it makes people draw close and love us.

When I studied group counseling, I learned a really inter-esting concept: if there is a group of people and one person decides to take a risk in sharing a vulnerable piece of his or her story, he or she instantly becomes the most popular member of the group. Why? It's called "universality." Every person in a group has traits or experiences or flaws or past mistakes that he or she wants to hide. When we see another take a bold risk and be accepted, we wish we had the guts to be that authentic. Of course, this concept could be taken to an extreme. It would not be prudent for a member to go into a group and reveal everything too quickly without get-ting to know the others. But one brave soul's gentle unveil-ing of a vulnerable truth can offer the ripple effect of relief and acceptance to others.

"BIG SHAME" INVITED TO THE KING'S TABLE

I'd like to end this chapter with one of my favorite Bible stories, found in 2 Samuel 9 (*THE MESSAGE*). David was king at this time. His best friend Jonathan was dead, as was Jonathan's father, King Saul. "One day David asked, 'Is there anyone left of Saul's family? If so, I'd like to show him some kindness in honor of Jonathan'" (v. 1). Because of his love for Jonathan, David wanted to find Jonathan's relatives.

"Ziba told the king, 'Yes, there is Jonathan's son, lame in both feet'" (v. 3). Earlier in the story we learn that when this boy, Mephibosheth, was five years old, his nurse heard that his father and grandfather were dead. She fled and dropped him, breaking both of his legs and leaving him crippled.

When Mephibosheth was found and brought before David, he bowed deeply, abasing himself, honoring David. He probably sensed that he might die, since he had heir rights to the throne as Saul's grandson.

Now here's where it gets good. David spoke his name: "Mephibosheth." His name means "big shame." Can you imagine what Mephibosheth felt like when he was in front of the king's throne and heard the king call him "Big Shame"? This, to me, is a picture of coming face-to-face with your whole self—the good and the bad—as I did, and as Rich Mullins did in the train station.

> "Don't be frightened," said David. "I'd like to do something special for you in memory of your father Jonathan. To begin with, I'm returning to you all the properties of your grandfather Saul. Furthermore, from now on you'll take all your meals at my table."

Shuffling and stammering, not looking him in the eye, Mephibosheth said, "Who am I that you pay attention to a dead dog like me?"

David then called in Ziba, Saul's right-hand man, and told him, "Everything that belonged to Saul and his family, I've handed over to your master's grandson. You and your sons and your servants will work his land and bring in the produce, provisions for your master's grandson. Mephibosheth himself, your master's grandson, from now on will take all his meals at my table." (vv. 7-9)

The story ends with this beautiful note: "Mephibosheth lived in Jerusalem, taking all his meals at the king's table. He was lame in both feet" (v. 13).

If Big Shame could find a place at the King's table, lame feet and all, I know we can too.

TIPS FOR SHARING YOUR SECRETS

- Healthy people don't see themselves at opposite ends of a pendulum—that is, either all good or all bad. They see themselves as human—flawed but worthy to give and to receive.
- Stop demanding love from others. Instead, begin to love yourself enough so that you can give yourself what you need.
- Tell your story. Find a counselor, friend, pastor, or mentor to whom you can tell your whole story.
- Understand that people's choices don't happen in a vacuum. People's choices make sense in light of their history. There's a reason people do what they do, and when we know their story it makes sense.

- Look in the mirror and say nice things. Frederick Beuchner tells us, "The grace of God means something like: Here is your life. You might never have been, but you are because the party wouldn't have been complete without you" (*Wishful Thinking*, 39).
- Allow yourself to be flawed. Even if you tried to be perfect, you wouldn't be. Be vulnerable, messy, and real, and watch how people draw near. Make sure people understand you're not coming to them to fix everything. You're just coming to them in authenticity.
- Be a safe person for others to tell their story to. Try listening without offering advice, platitudes, or Scripture. Sure, there's a time for those things, but mostly what people need is safety.

In the next chapter, we will look at the renewal that can come to us through appreciating beauty.

CHAPTER 7

RENEWED THROUGH APPRECIATING BEAUTY

I cannot believe that the inscrutable universe turns on an axis of suffering; surely the strange beauty of the world must somewhere rest on pure joy!

—LOUISE BOGAN

IT HAPPENS WHEN I hear Steve Green sing "Non Nobis Domine" or Jackie Evancho sing "Pie Jesu." It happened when, during the 2010 winter Olympics, Thomas Saulgrain performed on the high wire over the wheat fields to Joni Mitchell's haunting song "Both Sides Now." It happened when I looked into the hospital bassinette and stared into the blue eyes of my newborn child. It happened in a dark college auditorium when I felt God wooing me with Renaissance art on a gigantic screen.

You know the moments I'm talking about: the times when you see and appreciate beauty, and chills roll up your spine, and hair prickles on the back of your neck. Maybe tears fill your eyes. These are mysterious moments when you know there is something bigger and truer than any of us can see. More than a century ago, psychologist and philosopher William James described appreciation of beauty and excellence as a mystical experience in which one feels a sense of truth, oneness with the universe, an inability to express experience in mere words, and a vividness and clarity of sensation and perception. In his poem "Break, Break, Break," the poet Alfred, Lord Tennyson expressed the same struggle to adequately convey beauty:

> Break, break, break,
> On thy cold gray stones, O Sea!
> And I would that my tongue could utter
> The thoughts that arise in me.

Beauty is directly related to self-care because it is one of the few things that can break us out of our routine and make us think about eternity. Recently I read a fictional story that weaved in actual accounts from the life of Saint Francis of Assisi. Here is a passage from the book:

> *Beauty* can break a heart and make it think about something more spiritual than the mindless routine we go through day after day to get by. Francis was a singer, a poet, an actor. He knew that the imagination was a stealth way into people's souls, a way to get all of us to think about God. For him, beauty was its own apologetic. That's why a church should care about

the arts. They inspire all of us to think about the eternal. (Cron, *Chasing Francis*, 198)

In the movie *The Shawshank Redemption*, when Andy Dufresne reminds the prisoners of their humanity by playing an aria over the prison's public address system, every man freezes as the narrator, Red, recalls the moment:

> I have no idea to this day what those two Italian ladies were singing about. Truth is, I don't wanna know. Some things are best left unsaid. I'd like to think they were singing about something so beautiful it can't be expressed in words and makes your heart ache because of it. I tell you those voices soared higher and farther than anybody in the great place dares to dream. It was like some beautiful bird flapped in our drab little cage and made those walls dissolve away. And for the briefest of moments, every last man at Shawshank felt free.

BEAUTY HAS A PURPOSE

Throughout the course of Western history, philosophers have argued about the importance of beauty. An appreciation of beauty involves noticing and appreciating beauty and excellence in various domains—from art to nature to mathematics, to science to ordinary moments—and finding, recognizing, and taking pleasure in the existence of goodness in the physical and social worlds. Poets and philosophers have frequently written about the interweaving of truth, beauty, and goodness.

Some people can sustain beautiful moments by anticipating, accentuating, and deliberately remembering them, instead of just reacting to them. Experts have found that the ability to savor beautiful and positive experiences is one of the most important ingredients for happiness. Those who are inclined to notice an exquisite moment are less likely to experience guilt, stress, depression, and shame. And those who are able to rekindle the joy of past events are best able to buffer stress. Psychologists have discovered that people who are open to the beauty and excellence around them are more likely to find joy, meaning, and profound connections in their lives. Years ago, at a cozy bed and breakfast in Vermont, I had a discussion with our server. "I didn't used to believe in God," he said. "But seeing Van Gogh's *Starry Night* made me believe that maybe there could be a God."

Perhaps beauty's purpose is to buffer the pain and discouragement of life. It doesn't surprise me that medical researchers have discovered that patients who listen to music show immediate and marvelous responses such as reduced blood pressure and heart rate, less need for pain medication, and reduction of stress hormones.

Most people have had the experience of being in a funk, but when an upbeat song came on, their brain waves changed and their mood lifted. I was mindlessly jogging this morning, but when Joshua Radin's "Brand New Day" came on, my heart felt weightless and my step quickened. Music softens the edges of a hard world.

Maybe beauty's purpose is to shine like a diamond, radiant against a black backdrop, reminding us that something better is coming. In a world filled with stress and tragedy, a baby's giggle, a snow-kissed mountain, an amber sunset, the New England foliage, a Celtic reel, the smell of blooming lilacs, and any number of beautiful things touch us and give us respite from a difficult world.

BEAUTY OFFERS BENEFITS

Some researchers believe that appreciating beauty appears to have adaptive or survival value. On the surface, beauty appears to have no function. It doesn't keep us warm or pay the bills. However, beauty does relax the soul: because religions have inspired great music, art, and architecture, this suggests that there is a connection between the appreciation of beauty and experiences of transcendence. Other studies have found that as levels of engagement with beauty increase, a person's gratitude grows stronger, spiritual transcendence grows loftier, and life is more satisfying in general. Also, the higher the level of perception of something as morally beautiful, the greater the motivation becomes for humans to live moral lives as well.

The famous psychologist Abraham Maslow theorized that people's needs are prioritized. Unless the most basic needs are satisfied, they cannot focus on higher needs. The most basic needs are biological (food, water, oxygen), followed by needs for security, then love and belonging, and self-esteem. At the very top of the pyramid are the needs Maslow says belong to a self-actualized person—that is, when all other needs are satisfied, self-actualizers describe peak experiences such as beauty. But I believe all people—rich or poor, unloved or cared for—are informed by, benefit from, and deserve the benefits of beauty. Best of all, for anyone seeking those benefits, the most beautiful things are free.

Most of us are able to recognize something beautiful, but trying to describe what makes it so is much more difficult. Think about it. What is it about a particular scene, painting, or song that makes it beautiful? Some have tried to understand beauty by reducing it to lines and proportions. Others say the response toward beauty lies in the beholder—the reason something touches someone is because it is filtered through the lens of life experiences. Beauty is further complicated: I might find something beautiful today because it is new or unique, but being exposed to something day after day lessens its impact. A sad or melancholic mood may prime me to notice a particular landscape, book, or song. Being with someone I love may heighten my experience of beauty in an ordinary moment.

Sometimes beauty comes from the sum being greater than its parts. For instance, when certain songs and images are paired, the effect can be mesmerizing; but each one by itself may leave us lacking. We are more likely to enjoy a concert if we are in a beautiful setting, a meal when in the company of those we love, or the landscape if we just got good news. Recently I read a 1930s cookbook whose author captured the beauty of his dinner. After describing a relaxing way to cook dinner, he writes (albeit, before the time when cigarettes were known to be so detrimental):

> Now everything's done . . . or should I say, now everything can begin. Put the coffee pot on the burner for 20 seconds, but make sure the coffee doesn't boil, whatever you do. Pour a little boiling water into your coffee cup, then throw the water out. Fill your cup with the hot coffee. Lean back in your armchair and put your feet up. Light a cigarette. Take a nice long puff, then blow the smoke to the ceiling. Enjoy the coffee's aroma, take a long sip. Close your eyes. Think about that second puff, that second sip—you're rich!

In the background the radio's playing a tango or some jazz. (de Pomiane, *French Cooking in Ten Minutes*, 24–25)

Sometimes a certain encounter with beauty is so profound that we don't even want to describe it, for mere words and descriptions muddle it. When we find ourselves in the presence of beauty, we don't want to analyze what makes it beautiful. Instead we want to savor it and surrender to it. We want to capture it, prolong it, and enter it more deeply. Perhaps we should take Thornton Wilder's counsel: "My advice to you is not to inquire why or whither, but just enjoy your ice cream while it's on your plate."

BEAUTY LEADS US TO GOD

My sense is that beauty cannot be fully described because it is a mystery that is linked to God. I don't have proof of this; but whenever I am touched by beauty, I think about things like God, eternity, and heaven. C. S. Lewis talked about the longing we all have for beauty:

> We do not want merely to see beauty, though, God knows, even that is bounty enough. We want something else which can hardly be put into words—to be united with the beauty we see, to pass into it, to receive it into ourselves, to bathe in it, to become part of it. (Martindale and Root, *The Quotable Lewis*, 65)

Maybe beauty isn't even in the object itself, but rather in what the object represents. Beauty is the metaphor for God. All cultures celebrate beauty, and all humans yearn for something more. This is powerful proof that there is something more; otherwise we would not ache for it. The world conveys a message: "I know you can't fully grasp this, but someday you will." In Scripture, God's glory and beauty are often paired together. For example, King David proclaimed: "Ascribe to the LORD the glory due his name; / worship the LORD in the splendor of his holiness" (Psalm 29:2).

Years ago, I wanted to understand how George Frideric Handel wrote something so sublime as the *Messiah* oratorio—a work that takes three hours to perform. In my research I discovered that a friend of his compiled words from Scripture and gave them to him. Handel was so overcome by the power of the words that the music burst forth from him. He shut himself inside for three weeks, often forgetting to eat. My sense is that God picks people and venues through which God reveals beauty. Beauty deepens our enjoyment of life and heightens our longing for God.

TIPS FOR ADDING BEAUTY TO YOUR WORLD

Adding more beauty to your life is one powerful form of self-care. Here are a few ways to get started:

- Don't rely only on food, material items, and sex to "fill the void." Your soul may be longing for beauty. Pay attention to your real, underlying desires.
- Look through a photo album. Notice how many happy times you've had, and wonder about what made those times beautiful.

- Relish ordinary experiences such as eating a meal, walking to the bus stop on a snowy day, or taking a lavender bubble bath.
- Close your eyes and transport yourself back to a favorite memory.
- Be mindful of the present moment. Martial arts and yoga are powerful tools that can help you do this. Don't multitask—enjoy the one thing you are doing right now.
- Take pleasure in your senses. Notice the smell of cinnamon toast and the grass after a rainstorm. Chew your warm chocolate chip cookie, and don't do anything else. Close your eyes while listening to music. Wear earplugs to an art museum. Get a massage, pedicure, or facial. The five senses are the portals for feeding ourselves beauty.
- Pay attention to the transient and bittersweet. Just before my daughter graduated from college I posted this on her Facebook wall: "In the rush toward the future, don't forget to savor the fleeting moments of college life. Spend time with friends, take pictures, notice the scenery on the way to class."
- Keep a journal. Writing forces us to organize and integrate our thoughts. It also helps us prolong and enjoy (and return to) the memory.
- Surround yourself with morally beautiful people. We become like those we spend time with.
- Surround yourself with objects that give you pleasure. Thomas Moore suggests: "Living artfully might require taking the time to buy things with soul for the home. Good linens, a special rug, or a simple teapot can be a source of

enrichment not only in our own life, but also in the lives of our children and grandchildren" (*Care of the Soul*, 287).

- Lie on a blanket in your backyard. Read a book. Stare at the sky.
- Go to the park and watch children play. Notice their innocence.
- Recognize that less is more. Neutral drapes can accentuate a gorgeous chair. Succulent pears and rich blue cheese, or melon wrapped in salty prosciutto, can be better than a heavy feast.
- Spend time in nature. God is the master artist.
- Read beautiful books. Here's a start: *The Red Tent* by Anita Diamant, *Gilead* by Marilyn Robinson, and *Cold Tangerines* by Shauna Niequist.
- Spend your money only on things you love. Some of my favorite purchases have been bath salts from the Dead Sea, photo greeting cards from the Isabella Stewart Gardner Art Museum, and a hand-knit wool sweater from Ireland.

Let me end with this good word from John Eldredge:

> We need beauty; that's clear enough from the fact that God has filled the world with it. He has given us sun and rain, "wine that gladdens the heart of man, oil to make his face shine, and bread that sustains his heart" (Psalm 104:15).
>
> We need to drink in beauty wherever we can get it—in music, in nature, in art, in a great meal shared. These are all gifts to us from God's generous heart. Friends, those things are not decorations to a life; they bring us life. (*Waking the Dead*, 214)

Next, we will consider the important renewing benefits of play in self-care.

CHAPTER 8

RENEWED THROUGH PLAY

The opposite of play isn't work. It's depression.

—BRIAN SUTTON-SMITH

THE TODDLER SITTING IN THE BATHTUB leaned forward and waved at the dachshund that stood on two legs peering into the water. The dog barked and bowed forward each time the child waved his hand, sending the child into fits of laughter. As the game continued on my computer screen, I began laughing as hard as the child. I clutched my aching stomach and felt my eyes wet with happiness. When I showed my husband, he too erupted with laughter. Most of you have seen these silly videos in forwarded e-mails or on Facebook. We watch them because they make us happy. When do we lose that *joie de vivre*? At what point does life stop being fun and silly? When do we learn to stop playing?

WHAT IS PLAY?

Play is difficult to describe. It is done for its own sake; often it is purposeless. It is voluntary and pleasurable, and it happens when we feel trust and safety. It takes us into a state where we aren't watching the clock, and hours pass without our being aware of it; a state where we aren't thinking about ourselves or interrupted by extraneous thought, and work seems effortless; a state called "flow."

The term *flow* was coined and made famous by happiness expert Mihaly Csikszentmihalyi. He did an interesting study where subjects who were randomly beeped had to write down what they were doing and how happy they were. He found that people were not happiest during leisure time, as would be expected. Instead, they were happiest when they were doing an activity where they felt challenged yet in which they excelled; oftentimes it was work. There are many types of play, and not all playful activities benefit participants. Consider that cranky golfer cursing over each whack of his club. Surely he is not enjoying his play. Play is a state, and it must fit your temperament; it must give you an emotional boost. Here are just a few examples of play:

- Body play—dancing, hiking, walking, tennis
- Object play—building, sculpting, gardening,
- Social play—flirtation, pub talk, verbal kidding, games
- Transformative play—conducting a symphony, writing a novel, making a scrapbook

What play is for one person might not be play for another. Have you ever seen someone teach a subject or a skill for which they have a deep passion? The topic may be tedious and difficult, and yet there are some teachers who seem giddy, almost dancing, as they impart their information. For them, work is play.

MY MOST PLAYFUL DAY

I'll never forget one of my most fun, playful days ever. My husband and his colleague were invited to Cambridge, Massachusetts, to give a talk about property tax valuation. I joined my husband on the trip. The morning of my most playful day, I pulled on my sweats and running shoes and jogged along the Charles River in rain that was just about to turn into snow. Crew teams rowed their pencil-thin boats in unison. Red leaves crunched under my feet. I felt as though I were in a movie. Then I showered and caught a cab, which took me to Harvard's medical school where I met psychiatrist Judith Herman, whose work with trauma victims I respect. She invited me to sit in during group supervision with other clinicians.

After the meeting, I was heading back to our hotel when an Irish lad stopped to ask where I was from, and we quickly moved into conversation. As we visited, I told him of my special interest in working with victims of trauma. When he briefly described his own traumatic upbringing, we both felt that our encounter had been a "God meeting." I was able to refer him to a world-renowned clinic that offered counseling for free.

The next stop on my most playful day was the Isabella Stewart Gardner Museum. Ms. Gardner owned one of the world's best collections of art, housed in a building designed as a replica of a lavish fifteenth-century Venetian-style palace with three stories of galleries surrounding a sun- and flower-filled courtyard. I found myself lost in a state of flow, looking at world-famous art. Eventually I tired and found a quaint café in the basement. There, sipping lobster bisque, I giggled with ecstasy and reflected on my day. No, my best day wasn't about lying on a beach doing nothing. Instead it involved being fully engaged in something I was passionate about, and it brought meaning and purpose to my life. My most playful day would have been incredibly boring to some; but for me, allowing the day to simply unfold as I followed my whims and desires without much of an agenda (other than meeting the therapist) had been pure bliss.

LACK OF PLAY IS HARMFUL

In 1966, psychiatrist Stuart Brown was one of several experts asked to determine what had caused Charles Whitman, the Texas Tower Sniper, to first fatally stab his mother and wife in their homes, and then kill fourteen others in a ninety-minute shooting spree. (In addition to those victims, he wounded thirty-two others at the University of Texas in Austin.) What did Brown and his colleagues discover about Whitman? An abusive father had beaten Whitman's natural tendency for play out of him. As a child Whitman was forced into a rigid schedule of piano practice in order to perform for his father's friends. He grew up in a rigid, joyless atmosphere, deprived of opportunities for play.

Brown became convinced that play is not trivial. The great paradox of play is that it is purposeless yet provides immense psychological, social, and physical benefits. Brown spent many more years studying male murderers within the prison system of Texas. Time after time he found this specific population had either been deprived of or had abnormal play situations.

Brown's forty-five-plus years of research convinced him that play teaches us how to be more flexible and adaptable. It teaches us how to role-play, react to stress, become resilient, blow off steam, problem solve, and imagine. It is key to helping us learn how to regulate our emotions. Imaginary games prepare us for stressful scenarios in life— we learn to develop humor in a world we can't control. Play also seems to be necessary for developing the trust, cooperation, and common goal-setting that are essential for community.

According to Brown, all mammals play. Check out videos on YouTube showing dogs sliding down water slides when their owners are at work, monkeys enjoying hot springs in Japan, bear cubs wrestling, and big dogs gently nipping at little pups. But, of all mammals, human beings are at the top of the play heap.

PLAY AT THE OFFICE

Increasingly more companies are recognizing that bored or stressed-out workers are prone to burnout and lack creativity—and some companies are making a significant change. Last winter I joined my daughter and husband on a tour of the New Belgium Brewing Company in Fort Collins, Colorado. Our tour guide described how more than two hundred people apply for each job at this playful company. He himself had spent ten years applying. Here's why: all new employees get a coveted cruiser bicycle, and they receive stock in the publicly held company. As we worked our way through the headquarters, we noticed climbing walls, sporadically placed foosball tables, and corkscrew slides to take you from the second floor to the first. There is even a director of fun, whose *raison d'etre* is to make New Belgium a fun place to work. And all this fun and play has benefits for the work itself. As Martin Seligman, happiness psychologist, states, "Positive mood produces broader attention . . . more creative thinking . . . and more holistic thinking . . . in contrast to negative mood which produces narrower attention . . . more critical thinking, and more analytic thinking."

PLAY IN FAMILIES

Our society may be losing some of the play benefits that previous generations took for granted. Now parents drive their children from one activity to another and to structured play dates. But when do children let their minds rest? In many traditional schools, classes such as physical education, art, and music are almost extinct. When do children have idle time to pretend? When are all five senses engaged? How many children play ball in the streets or climb trees? A world of limited play affects not only children but adults as well.

Play is not frivolous. Dr. Mark Epstein, in his book *Open to Desire*, shares a story of living in New York City in the aftermath of 9/11. The worst wreckage was right outside his family's window, and for months they had to pass through police and army checkpoints. Worry and agitation were a normal part of their day. On a prior trip to Tucson, Dr. Epstein's young son acquired a stuffed animal named Hoss. The animal became a transitional object—a bridge to conversation—between father and son. Father would speak in a western accent, as if he were the stuffed animal talking. A couple of nights after the terrorist attack, with sirens blaring below their home, the boy said to his toy, "Hey Hoss, did you hear what happened to the World Trade Center?" Dr. Epstein suddenly became alert and responded in a western accent as if he were Hoss speaking: "Can't say I have, Little Pardner. What happened to the World Trade Center?" After his son relayed the horrible events, Hoss answered, "What are you talking about, Little Pardner? Terrorists, hijackings, buildings collapsing! Listen to you. What kind of imagination do you have? People don't fly airplanes into skyscrapers, you know that!" The playful interaction was a way for father and son to process the unimaginable events. In an emotional release they experienced the first laughter since the twin towers came down.

"While trauma and threat tend to take away the desire for playfulness," Epstein insists, "they intensify the need for it." He continues to say that "play is one of those things, like dreaming, that seems superfluous but that we cannot seem to live without" (*Open to Desire*, 154–56).

Play is critical to self-care and possibly even to survival. Neuroscience research is just beginning to understand how good play is for us. Brain scans show that the brain "lights up" when it is at play. Play may help with thinking, memory, and of course stress.

A potent self-care tool, play encourages positive emotions and allows people to build relationships at a higher rate than expected. Play helps children and adults with emotional and social skills. They learn to think creatively, spontaneously, and abstractly. Both groups learn to express their feelings and to experiment with role-play. Play helps relieve boredom and tension. It helps prevent aggression and creates intimacy between people. For anyone who has suffered from trauma, play is a necessary gift. So many times, in spite of difficult sessions, deep laughter has brought profound healing to my clients.

WE ARE DRAWN TO PLAYFUL PEOPLE

Gina is a walking party. Everything she does is playful. She is a corporate speaker who has been paid heftily to talk about the funny things that find their way into her life. One morning she wandered out to her backyard and saw a team of hot air balloonists, who offered her a ride. When her husband woke up, he went outside looking for her. There she was, way up in the sky! He stood there scratching his head.

Gina decided to take up kickboxing, and was put into a competition with the one other forty-year-old woman who was competing. Gina's first punch caused the other woman to grunt, at which point Gina apologized. Soon the two women were doubled over in laughter when they realized their attributes of compassion and friendship were going to interfere with the competition. Every day Gina plays, and when she walks into a room, people want to laugh and play with her. Playful people attract others like bees to honey.

Near the end of my regular yoga class, after all the balancing and stretching, we reach the part that we all look forward to—the part where we hold the position "happy baby." Those of you who are familiar with yoga know this is a vulnerable position, to say the least. Lying flat on your back, you grab both feet with knees flayed open. Our instructor guides us to close our eyes and to get lost in the pose as she encourages us to gently roll on our backs from side to side in that position. "Haaaappppy baby girls," she sometimes says, adding, "And can you believe we get to do this while some people are sitting at their desk doing the corporate grind?"

Play in all its forms (laughter; yoga; imagination; accepting new adventures; connecting to others) keeps our child-heart alive and ticking. It is one of the most pleasurable forms of self-care. So, what can you play today?

TIPS FOR ADDING PLAY TO YOUR DAY

- Do something spontaneous just because you feel like it in the moment.

- Spend time doing things you enjoy, things that challenge you, and things that make you lose track of time.
- Make a "bucket list." Write down twenty things you want to do before you die. Start making plans to do one of the items on your list.
- Laugh deeply. It's amazing how good you'll feel if you do.
- Deliberately schedule fun into your life. If you don't, it won't happen.
- Spend time with others. Make sure they are people you like and enjoy. Remember, we become like those we hang around.
- Think of things that involve music, nature, moving your body, and using your sense of humor.
- Create something: a poem, a story, a song, or a garden.

Remember the words of Heraclitus: "Man is most nearly himself when he achieves the seriousness of a child at play."

In the next chapter we'll look at the renewing benefits of exercise.

CHAPTER 9

RENEWED
THROUGH EXERCISE

Those who think they have not time for bodily exercise will sooner or later have to find time for illness.

—EDWARD STANLEY

I WAS IN HIGH SCHOOL, enduring some of the most stressful times of my life. My mother was in the last few years of a terminal illness. My father, a doctor, gave his time and attention to his patients, leaving little left for his seven children. Our family was hanging together, but bonding and communicating wasn't our strength.

During that time, my father started waking me up early. "Get up, we're going running," he'd say, and I didn't dare tell him no. I would look at the clock and notice that the first number was smaller than six, but I would drag myself out of bed, stumble around trying to find anything warm, and head out the door with him.

I'm sure there were a few nice days, though I can't remember any. I remember steep embankments of snow, and icy wind whipping the vestiges of skin exposed to the elements. We didn't talk much, so the noises were reduced to audible breaths in syncopated rhythm and a few grunts for good measure. Every so often a car would drive by and honk. My dad and I didn't even look to see whom we were addressing; we just raised our gloved hands. I think our runs averaged three to five miles per day, every day except weekends, when Dad let me sleep in.

Despite the early and the cold, those runs began to give me a sense of achievement. I was experiencing the euphoric feeling of endorphins and physical fitness. I was also getting special treatment and attention that the other six kids were not. And I discovered, too, that I was beginning to lose weight. I remember trying on a pair of slim pink corduroy pants, and they fit. Suddenly, I was hooked on running.

Since then running has become part of my daily life, bringing overall happiness, good health, time for prayer and my creative process, and relief from anxiety.

EXERCISE COUNTERACTS STRESS

Stress is the body's way of rising to a challenge and preparing to meet a tough situation with focus, strength, stamina, and heightened alertness. Not all stress is bad. For example, the stress response (also called the fight-or-flight response) is critical during emergency situations, such as when a driver has to slam on the brakes to avoid an accident or when a student needs to study for an important exam. Yet chronic stress keeps the body's nervous system activated, and that's like having a car motor that is revved up for too long. Initially the body can rise to the challenge, but eventually it breaks down. Stress hormones can leave a person feeling depleted and overwhelmed, weaken the immune system, cause weight gain, increase blood pressure, and raise the risk of heart attacks and strokes. The body's stress reaction can also cause brain changes that contribute to depression, anxiety, and addiction.

Probably the best way to counteract the negative effects of stress is through exercise. It is especially helpful for those who are stressed, anxious, or depressed. In addition to reducing levels of stress hormones, exercise stimulates the production of endorphins, the body's natural painkiller and mood elevator.

The benefits of exercise are exponential. Exercise helps you to lose weight and strengthens bones and muscles. With exercise you help boost your self-image. Feeling good about yourself reduces emotional stress. And physical activity deepens breathing and releases muscle tension, which also makes you feel good.

Exercise also gives you the chance for renewal, a minivacation from work and worry. For many, the rhythmic experience of jogging or running is meditative. Many people say they have their most creative thoughts while working out, as well.

Thirty minutes of moderate physical activity a day could:

- Improve your mood and mental functioning, and reduce stress.
- Lower your risk of developing hypertension and diabetes.
- Reduce your risk for cancer, especially colon and breast cancer.
- Reduce your chance of getting heart disease.
- Help you maintain independence in your later years.
- Help you maintain a healthy weight.
- Improve your sex life.
- Improve your ability to recover from colds
- Help you fall asleep faster and sleep more deeply.
- Cut your risk of depression in half.
- Turn on an appetite-stimulating hormone called ghrelin.
- Slow the aging process.
- Create an atmosphere for sunlight to lift your mood.

To be most effective, exercise should include four components:

1. Aerobic. This may include running, swimming, or walking at a fast clip.
2. Stretching. This keeps muscles limber and helps maintain their tone and strength. Yoga is a great way to focus on stretching.
3. Weight training. This helps rebuild bones by creating an electrical charge that ignites growth. A great way to get started is to take a class at a recreation center.

4. Building balance. There is a strong correlation between good balance and good memory. Experts believe balancing stimulates the neural network in your brain. Examples of ways to build balance are yoga and tai chi.

Although for many people *exercise* is something they avoid, one of the best ways to renew and replenish yourself is by reframing exercise as a great self-care tool. You may learn to love exercise—and the gift of balance, self-confidence, and energy that it provides.

TIPS FOR PUTTING EXERCISE INTO EACH DAY

- Work out first thing in the morning. You'll be more likely to do it then than you will be at the end of the day, when you are tired.
- Pair exercise with a pleasurable activity, such as meeting up with friends, listening to music or podcasts, reading a book, or watching TV on a treadmill.
- Vault over your negative thoughts. Think, *Thirty minutes from now I'm going to feel amazing!*
- Pick a form of exercise you enjoy so that you won't be tempted to skip it.
- Start. Most people don't really hate exercise; they hate the thought of exercise. Once you start it's actually enjoyable to feel your body move.
- Forget about finding time. Make the time! We all find time to do the things we deem important.
- Start small and add to your regimen. Walk for thirty minutes. Try adding strength training and stretching two to

three times a week. Yoga and stretchy bands are perfect for this.

- Say, "I get to do this," not, "I have to do this."
- Diversify your workout in order to work various muscle groups and to prevent boredom.
- Reward yourself after you meet goals.
- Recognize that you don't have to train for a marathon or do an extreme program; however, you should do moderate exercise for at least thirty minutes every day unless you are sick.
- Work out in the sunshine, if possible. Ultraviolet B rays enable your body to make vitamin D, and sunshine elevates mood and improves concentration. Use sunscreen.

In the next chapter, we will look at the important place that forgiveness holds in our self-care and renewal.

CHAPTER 10

RENEWED THROUGH FORGIVENESS

To forgive is to set a prisoner free and
discover the prisoner was you.

—LOUIS SMEDES

FOR YEARS I HAD BEEN CONSUMED with venom toward a special enemy; let's call her Jane. I won't go into the specific details, but this was a person our family had been generous to as she was going through a hard time. After a long period, we sensed that the woman wasn't moving on with her life and was taking advantage of our offer. When I confronted her, she laughed and scoffed. Then she moved on.

For years I was full of rage and hate, wishing we had never shown kindness to this woman. After many years of not seeing her, I discovered she was working at an establishment that I visited several times a week. I knew this was no coincidence; of all the places she could be, God had placed her there.

I hated having to see her, and had a knot in the pit of my stomach whenever I thought about her. But then I began having dreams of forgiveness. They were weird dreams that filled me with peace. Though I didn't want to forgive her, I began to hope that I would want to forgive her. However, I knew I could not do this in my human power, so I started to pray. After several painful weeks, we were camping with some friends, one of whom was our pastor. Surely he of all people would empathize with my pain. Instead, he said, "Lucille, I think God is leading you to a place of forgiveness."

I continued to pray. One afternoon I walked into the office across from my enemy, and there sat an old acquaintance. We began catching up, and he mentioned that he was learning what a blessing it was to suffer for the name of Christ. I thought of Jane (whom I had just seen) and laughed. Rather than continuing on with his story, he stopped short, looked at me, and asked what was so funny. I ended up telling him the whole story. He said, "Lucille, do you believe that God can speak to us in our dreams?" "Sure," I responded.

He pulled a small Bible out of his pocket and turned to a few passages about dreams. Suddenly, in that moment, I felt God had been compelling me in my dreams to seek reconciliation, and I told this friend so. I truly wanted to forgive but didn't know how, and in that moment I realized I had the support to do it. My friend said he would stay there and pray. His supportive presence and God's Spirit gave me courage as I rushed across the hall toward my offender, fearful that I might change my mind.

Shaking, I walked up to Jane and asked if I could speak with her privately. She looked around nervously and moved to a leather couch. I got on my knees, took her hands, and said, "I'm sorry for the trouble between us." I knew this wasn't about her as much as about getting my heart right; whatever she chose to do was between her and God. I continued, "Jane, I want to know you are doing well. Are you happy?" Newly married, she said she was very happy. Then she asked about my children and apologized for the way things had turned out.

After that incident, I began to release my anger toward her, and I no longer dreaded seeing her. If I crossed her path, I could simply smile and wave, wishing her well and meaning it. God set me free from consuming thoughts of hate and vengeance.

Some believe that if you murdered someone in ancient Rome, as a punishment, the dead person's body was strapped to you until it rotted away. Imagine the relief that would come if that putrid carcass were cut free. That's a picture of how I felt after forgiving this person. It was over.

THE EMOTIONAL AND PHYSICAL IMPACT OF UNFORGIVENESS

In clinical literature, unforgiveness is conceptualized as a stress reaction that has dire mental and physical consequences for the one who is offended and stuck in a place of unforgiveness. This kind of stress involves decreases in the brain's prefrontal cortex. Under stress our ability to think weakens. The body also reacts by increasing respiration, blood pressure, and heart rate. This stress decreases digestion, growth, and sexual hormones, and weakens the immune system.

When people are hurt they are likely to react with anger, resentment, hostility, bitterness, hatred, or fear. They try to find ways to narrow the gap by demanding apologies or restitution; renarrating (telling a different story or finding a different meaning); trying self-soothing or avoidance techniques; seeking personal or divine revenge; or legal or political justice. Creative people find many ways to move forward. One of the most powerful ways seems to be the act of forgiveness.

Forgiveness is a complex topic and may require unique steps for the individuals involved. As I examined my own forgiveness history, I noticed I arrived at forgiveness and moved forward in various ways. One time I had to seek legal restitution; another time I had to seek counseling; and in another instance I had to have someone stand in the gap while I offered first steps of forgiveness.

One of my friends had a wonderful way of arriving at forgiveness. She describes an incident that happened to her and how she responded: "Once when we got ripped off by an unscrupulous business, I could not let it go. So I found out when the employees and their boss had their weekly meeting, and I showed up with a platter of homemade cookies and a gracious note. They never apologized, and now I couldn't even tell you the name of that business. I did some-thing nice for them and walked away."

RUSH TO FORGIVE

Unfortunately, in the church we often rush people to for-give before they do the critical emotional work. This is spiri-tual abuse. Hurt people must tell their story in a safe place. They need a place to express anger, because anger is the alarm that shows a boundary was crossed. Hurt people need to be allowed to say, "This was not OK!" They need a wit-ness, a stand-in for Christ, to say, "I'm so sorry this happened to you." They need someone who will hurt with them and maybe even cry for them. They don't need an explanation or a platitude at this point. In fact, platitudes can further wound people. We have all heard of people who were clobbered with Romans 8:28 or told, "God must have a reason." It is only after we have done the hard work of forgiveness that those words make sense, for it is the release valve for those who've been hurt. In forgiving we are canceling the debt; we are essentially saying, "You don't owe me anymore."

BENEFITS OF FORGIVENESS

Science supports the idea that forgiveness is a strategy for reducing the ill effects of unforgiveness. Forgiveness has been defined as a reduction in negative emotion toward an offender. It is conceptualized as replacing the negative emotions with positive ones such as empathy, sympathy, compassion, or love.

If a pharmaceutical company developed a pill that could lower heart rate and blood pressure; decrease stress, fatigue, medication usage, and physical symptoms; improve sleep; strengthen spirituality; and reduce depression symptoms, we would all buy stock in that company. With the advent of brain imaging, researchers are able to see various parts of the brain "light up" when people forgive, especially areas that regulate emotional responses, moral judgments, perceptions of physical pain, and decision making.

Forgiveness is that drug, and the benefits are beyond the physical ones that I just listed. Forgiveness has been shown to promote positive thoughts, feelings, and behavior toward the offender. The benefits of forgiveness spill over to positive behaviors toward others outside of the relationship. Forgiveness is often associated with increased volunteerism, donations to charity, and other altruistic behaviors.

When people are able to forgive, they are empowered. Viktor Frankl, Corrie ten Boom, and Anne Frank showed they were stronger than the most unimaginable evil. No one could take away their capacity for hope, kindness, and faith. Forgiveness is ultimately a matter of choice. It leads to better health, less stress, more power, and happier relationships. Don't think about your enemy; think about you. Forgiveness is a matter of self-care.

MYTHS RELATED TO FORGIVENESS

There are many myths about forgiveness. For instance, some people believe that if you forgive, you are implying that you have to be involved in the offender's life.

Forgiveness is about the past, but reconciliation is about the future. Keep the time sequence separate. You may not be able to reconcile with someone until they own their transgression, but you can always forgive someone. Also, forgiveness is not necessarily about the other person. It is about moving toward your own healing.

At this point you may be saying, "Well, it's not fair. How can someone be allowed to hurt me, but then I have to be the one to forgive?" You're right; it's not fair. But the painful words or events already happened. You can't undo them. What's not fair is for you to suffer even more physical and emotional pain than you have to. The only thing that will fix that pain is for you to forgive. Some have said that harboring bitterness and unforgiveness is like drinking poison and expecting the other person to die. When you forgive, you are the one who benefits.

Maybe you believe that the other person has to say "sorry" in order for you to forgive. This is another myth. The perpetrator may be gloating or unrepentant. Forgiveness is still the goal and still possible. Obviously the greater the offense, the longer and more difficult the journey to forgiveness seems to be. In working with clients, I have discovered that the people who move forward seem to ask the question how rather than why. They pour their energy into something that makes the world better, rather than surrendering to bitterness or circular thinking.

Here's another myth: just say the forgiving words and move on. Yet, forgiveness is a journey. Picture forgiveness like an onion—we move through it one layer at a time. You can follow the course of forgiveness through my story that opened this chapter: first, angst was created in my life; then there was the presence of dreams; and then finally the help of others became a scaffold to moving closer to forgiveness.

Whatever your own path, remember that even when you think you've forgiven, there will most likely be times of recurring hurt or anger; but it will lessen each time, and you will move through each recurrence more quickly.

Another myth is that forgiveness is for sissies. If you've ever accomplished the task of forgiveness, you know nothing could be further from the truth. Forgiveness is one of the most difficult tasks a human being can do. In fact, I believe that in many cases we cannot do it without divine help. Sometimes we don't even have the ability to pray for the desire to ask God to help us want to forgive. But we can pray like this: "God, soften my heart, and make me want to begin asking you how to *begin* forgiving this person." Sometimes, we just submit the smallest amount in prayer, and God creates opportunities for the rest to happen.

FORGIVING YOURSELF

Like many people, I was able to accept God's forgiveness but I was unable to forgive myself. My pastor and I recently had a conversation about this, and he said he believes the church is filled with people who can't forgive themselves. Remember, being unforgiving, even to yourself, takes a huge toll on your physical and emotional health. Though I had committed my life to God, I was stuck with the inability to forgive myself for my past. I told my pastor that what helped me finally forgive myself was being able to tell my story and have insight into why I did the things I did. Understanding why I reacted the way I did wasn't a way to minimize sin in my life, but it did help me finally forgive myself. I hadn't learned a better way to cope." This allowed me to begin to offer myself the grace I tried to extend to others.

Another reason we struggle to forgive ourselves is that we set the perfection bar high. When I didn't reach the bar, I saw myself as all bad. When I did reach it, I saw myself as all good. By talking about our dark sides, we begin to realize that every person has a good side and a bad side. Just because we don't show the dark side to others or to ourselves doesn't mean it's not there.

As a counselor, I've developed a definition of *mental health:* when people can easily admit to their strengths and deficits. *Pathology* is when people only see one side—all good or all bad. Healthy people are able to goof up, own their mistakes, admit to them, and even laugh about some of them. Those with a healthy psyche speak gracefully to themselves: "I am a human being having a human experience."

For me, when life hurt during that time of unforgiveness, I told myself it was because I was evil to my core. Those were summations that I concluded and that I daily scanned my world to confirm.

But in the safety of a good counselor's office, I had a corrective emotional experience. What was reflected back to me was this: "You are worthy of love," "I am so sorry for your losses," and, "You are not the sum of your mistakes." As God's kind of love flowed toward me, I began to love and forgive myself. I could not have forgiven myself alone—I understood it had to be in relationship with others.

"Lucille," my counselor told me, "the only one who can throw stones (he said, referring to Christ) is you. You daily pick up the biggest rock and beat yourself with it." Later that afternoon, after meeting with him, I picked up the biggest, most jagged rock I could find and launched it into the lake. As the water splashed back on me, I let self-forgiveness begin to wash over me.

A word of caution here: if you sense in any way that the person you are telling your story to is shaming you, find another counselor immediately. Some types of counseling use shaming as a technique for helping people grow. Having interacted with supervisors who followed this practice, I can tell you that shaming does not help shame-based people; it makes them want to crawl back into the dark. You still may feel shame telling your story, but make sure you tell your story to someone who will not shame you. And note: shaming is different from confrontation—sometimes counselors do confront clients who are causing harm to themselves or others.

One of the ways I work with clients to help them forgive themselves is to look with them at how they perhaps took on badness and shame that was never theirs in the first place. Maybe a parent or someone else gave it to them. But even though parents may not have done the job of loving and nurturing, a considerate counselor will help clients see a bigger picture: their parents, too, may not have gotten the love and nurture they should have.

The brain in crises reacts one of two ways: fight or flight. The brain makes people run or stay, but it doesn't give them the option or time to think it over. People will beat themselves up for not doing something heroic like standing up to an abusive father or not letting go of their friend in the water after a helicopter crash. The brain literally short-circuits the prefrontal cortex—the thinking part of the brain—and loops into the limbic (emotional), reacting part of the brain. Understanding that as I work with clients, I tell them, "Whatever your brain did in that moment was what it knew to do. It couldn't have done anything else."

Reframing is another tool counselors use to help people forgive themselves and others. For instance, a counselor might say something like, "Your coping technique at that time probably kept you alive, but now you don't need it anymore," or, "You say your parents only gave you fifty cents for your birthday, but in 1930 that was a lot of money." Of course, no one wants to reframe something that isn't true or is not helpful to the client.

Whatever the starting point or the tools for reframing, forgiveness toward yourself and others is a powerful self-care tool, a way to renew yourself. Forgiveness frees you to live your life well.

TIPS FOR FORGIVING

- Find someone to help you process your story. Anger and grief are necessary ingredients before forgiveness happens.
- Read helpful books about forgiveness. Lewis Smedes, Henry Cloud, John Townsend, and Dave Stoop all have written books dealing with the psychological side of forgiveness.

- Realize that forgiveness takes time and that it comes in layers.
- Practice tangible rituals: write out a list and burn it, or write a letter to yourself or to your offender. Read the letter out loud to someone safe, but don't send it. This allows the process to begin.
- If you are not ready to forgive, offer yourself grace.
- Continue telling yourself that forgiveness is the gift you will give yourself.
- Remind yourself that you cannot undo what happened. Instead of asking yourself why, ask yourself how (for example, "How can I use this experience?").
- Consider what Christ has done for your own sin.
- Ask God to begin helping you want to forgive.
- Speak gracefully to yourself and others.
- Read the list of affirmations from the chapter on emotional self-care.
- Watch movies about forgiveness: *Heaven's Rain, Amazing Grace, Les Miserables, An Unfinished Life*, and *End of the Spear* are a few.

In the next chapter we'll look at creating a space for grief as a means of self-care.

CHAPTER 11

RENEWED THROUGH CREATING A PLACE FOR GRIEF

When we become aware that we do not have to escape our pains, but that we can mobilize them into a common search for life, those very pains are transformed from expressions of despair into signs of hope.

—HENRI J. M. NOUWEN

BRIDGET CAME TO the counselor's office trying not to cry. Her baby had died shortly after being born. Initially she cried, but it upset her parents, who said her crying would upset her other child. Bridget held it in, prayed, and hoped her sadness would go away. Soon her sadness turned into fear and anxiety. She attended Bible studies, prayed, and listened to a popular pastor on the radio who said that depression was sin and that God promised power, love, and a sound mind (2 Timothy 1:7). As the months wore on, her symptoms grew worse instead of better; so she called her pastor, who led Bridget to Scripture about joy. He said she needed to claim the joy for herself. By the time she came to the counselor's office she was convinced her lack of faith kept her from getting better.

There are myriad ways that people get hurt—divorce, loss of loved ones, loss of jobs, injuries, breakups, abortion, natural disasters, and so forth—but there is really only one way to process grief. Rather than ignoring it or holding it in, grief must be dealt with. Studies show that trying not to think of something actually causes a person to dwell on it more, but in a way that cannot be attended to. When we attempt to keep our emotions under control, we actually allow them to control us.

GRIEF AND THE CHURCH

Many times Christians are taught to avoid emotional pain by being told, in so many words, that our emotions can't be trusted; therefore, we shouldn't acknowledge them. Teacher, counselor, and author Dan Allender says that the church continues to offer such alternatives as "denial-based forgiveness, pressured demands to love, and quick relief from pain through dramatic spiritual interventions." Then he adds, "The work of restoration cannot begin until a problem is fully faced" (Wounded Heart, 13–14).

The message from many churches is, "If you're doing bad things, change your thoughts," and, "If you're thinking bad things, change your behavior." Allender writes:

The assumption taught in many Christian groups is that emotions will follow in accord with your choice of will. If you feel angry, then do good, because in doing good you will eventually not be angry. Even better, they suggest, if you do good long enough, then you will actually feel loving emotions toward the person who did you harm. (*Wounded Heart*, 17)

What is missing in this equation is paying attention to the real feelings of anger, sadness, fear, regret, guilt, and joy.

The prophet Jeremiah warned that we cannot heal a wound by saying it's not there:

They dress the wound of my people
    as though it were not serious.
"Peace, peace," they say,
    when there is no peace. (Jeremiah 6:14)

But if feelings are so bad and so dangerous, then why did God make them? God made feelings so that we would express them. Expressing emotion plays a critical part in our emotional health. Wrestling with God in the midst of painful emotions such as anger and grief becomes the arena in which we can finally understand that life is hard but God is good. One of my counseling teachers drew a circle, which he titled "pain," on the dry-erase board. He drew arrows circling around the outside of the circle and then boomeranging off it, depicting how some people butt up to pain but then turn and run to the nearest distraction, such as addictions, to numb the pain. Sometimes people start to immerse themselves inside the circle of pain, but when the experience proves too painful, they run back out for safety. Hear me: the only way through pain is *through* it. Emotions move us (E + motion = movement).

When clients are swirling in the "perfect storm" of emotional pain, I often remind them that they will get through it and that it is worth it. People don't move through grief very well by doing it alone. Most of us need a guide who will honor our courage, witness our painful loss, and join us on the scary sojourn through the circle of pain. This is how real healing happens.

I've heard people ask, "I lived through it once, why should I go through it again?" Counseling helps by providing an environment in which people reexperience past pain in an arena of kindness, safety, and compassion. Clinicians offer reframes, insights, and salve for the wound. New neural networks are formed in the brain, allowing the wounded client to leave "the valley of the shadow of death" and finally find "green pastures and quiet waters." Of course, counseling will not remove the memory of a painful past; a scar will remain, but the wound will stop hemorrhaging.

The church sometimes facilitates a message of moving quickly through pain by handing over Scripture and platitudes instead of encouraging the wrestling match, instead of allowing the multitude of emotions to spill over our circumstances. Many people come to my office afraid to tell me about their anger toward God. I greet them with this: anger with the situation or with God can be healthy. Anger is the protest, the line in the sand that says, "This is not OK!" It is when a client can't get angry that there is more cause for worry. For anyone willing to do the wrestling, counselors create safe havens for clients to express all of their emotions—and they facilitate that wrestling match!

GRIEVING WELL

Pain arrives on everyone's doorstep. Loss is a natural part of life, whether it is the loss of a parent, a grandparent, or a pet. We've all experienced it to one degree or another. As Barbara Baumgardner in *A Passage through Grief* says, "Grief is not a problem to be cured. It is simply a statement that you have loved someone" (*A Passage Through Grief*, 1).

When you lose someone close to you, it's a pain that just won't go away. Grief is a journey that involves a lot of different emotions: shock, numbness, denial, crying, anger, resentment, fear, doubt, sorrow, and confusion. Discouragement and depression are normal parts of loss. But how many of us have ever taken the time to fully grieve the loss of someone close to us?

Imagine everyone practicing the Jewish ritual called "sitting shiva." Seven solid days are set aside for intense grieving. Mourners come together, sit low to the ground, and comfort one another with short visits called "shiva calls." Instead, most contemporary Americans are notorious for pulling themselves up by their bootstraps and carrying on. Denying emotions can work for a while, but emotions will work their way out in the form of anxiety, depression, or addictions.

The following are some important reminders for anyone who has lost a loved one.

Grief waits. In essence, grief is a job that you are assigned. It has a beginning, a middle, and an end, although you might always feel some sadness and loss. The image of moving through grief reminds me of the song lyrics, "When

you're goin' through hell, keep on walkin'." Some people
avoid the assignment, hoping that if they distract themselves
over a long enough period of time, the pain will go away.
They resort to drinking, gambling, shopping, and so on. All
of these coping techniques work in the moment, but over
the long run grief is still sitting there, waiting.

We heal in relationship. God created us to need other
people. I don't understand why, but we need someone else
to acknowledge what we are going through. Some of your
friends and family won't be able to help you, but many will.
Find someone who is willing to see your pain, hear your stories, and feel your regret. God has ordained that we grow
and be strengthened in our relationships with one another as
we find the people who exercise their God-given gifts
(1 Peter 4:10; Ephesians 4:16).

Let your loved one be real. Often we tend to idealize the
loved one that we have lost. After my mother died, I canon-
ized her. In my mind I made her a saint who had never done
any wrong. An important task in grieving means seeing the
person as he or she really was. It might be helpful to keep a
journal about your loved one's flaws or to make a collage
that shows his or her character deficits along with his or her
wonderful traits. Don't judge your emotions. At times you
may feel anger, rage, terror, hate, blame, and jealousy. You
may feel this at the same time you feel love, sorrow, loss,
and yearning. Acknowledge all your feelings; express them.
Some people try to squelch negative and painful emotions,
but this actually causes them to worsen.

Acknowledge your loss. The first feelings of peace appear
when you move to the acceptance stage of grief. Until then,

you agonize. Even Jesus went through this. In the garden he was in turmoil: "My soul is overwhelmed with sorrow to the point of death. . . . If possible . . . take this cup from me." But when he said, "Yet not what I will, but what you will," acceptance—peace, supernatural strength—entered (Mark 14:32-42). I should hasten to say that you can't "hurry up" the stages of grief, but just knowing that peace will come when you get to the acceptance stage is comforting. Inwardly you sigh and say, "This thing that I did not want or see coming has, indeed, happened to me. And God and I will also get through this together." Stop arguing with reality and try to accept it. Then God's blessed peace comes.

Grief takes time. You may feel that you will never get over the loss of your loved one. And you may even fear getting over this person because that might mean you are forgetting him or her. The good news is that you will never get over this person. As one helpful counselor told me, "He will always be a part of you, and you get to keep everything he gave you." Remind yourself that you really do want to move past this part that hurts so much, and then you will be able to enjoy and remember the person without so much pain. Grief peaks at three months, then again at twelve months. Grief typically lasts two to three years—and longer for parents who've lost children. It fades with time but never really goes away. But in Christ we have hope. Deuteronomy 33:27 says, "The eternal God is your refuge, / and underneath are the everlasting arms." The word *underneath* really translates as "eternal and forever, almost bottomless." You are never too low for God to lift you up. If grief turns into depression that doesn't relent, see a doctor. You may need antidepressants for a time.

Take time off from grief. Make sure you are taking time off to go exercise, to see a lighthearted movie with friends, and to get some sunshine. Make sure you are eating right. If you find yourself laughing, don't feel guilty. Laughter has many health benefits and releases needed endorphins into your body. Sunshine, fellowship, laughter, and exercise release the body's natural painkillers.

Learn to live with questions. Asking *What if?* only makes you feel crazy. Realize you may never have answers as to why God allowed this. As I mentioned before, one thing that helped me was learning to ask how and what, not why. How would God work through this loss? What could I learn during this time? Don't make major life decisions for at least a year if at all possible.

Take care of yourself. Caring for yourself is one of the best ways you can honor your loved one. Make time for sleep, eat a balanced diet, exercise, and spend time with people who will let you talk. Limit alcohol, caffeine, and sugar. Grief takes a huge emotional and physical toll, so you need to be proactive about self-care. Do the things that bring healing to you and that connect you to the people you love.

Let others help you. People who offer really do want to help. Rely on people you trust. Accept it when people offer to run your errands, meet you for coffee, bring you a meal, or babysit your children. If you've ever been on the giving side, you know how badly people want to feel needed during your difficult time; but others can't help unless they know how. Consider having a friend make a list and being a contact person so you don't have to use extra energy to receive help.

Find ways to memorialize your loved one. Planting a tree or creating a scholarship are powerful ways to ensure that the memory of your loved one goes on. Over the years you get to see the fruit and beauty that comes from something tangible.

Keep a journal. There has been a lot of research regarding the emotional and physical benefits for people who write about grief and trauma. Journaling is a very private experience where you are safe to write about whatever you are feeling. There are no rules other than you shouldn't worry about the rules of formal writing. Proper spelling, punctuation, and grammar should not be the focus of your writing. Some people write daily; others only when they need to express themselves. Some journal keepers divide their journal into sections, such as "Feelings," "Family Memories," "My Favorite Things," "Sources of Inspiration," "Things I Wish I Had Said," and so on. One resourceful woman bought a beautiful coffee-table book about fathers. Since she had had a difficult relationship with her father, she wrote in the page margins all the things she wished he had been to her. The journal becomes a resource for empowerment and inspiration as well as a therapeutic tool. Often words aren't adequate to express feelings, and you may need to express your feelings another way. Some people heal by painting, singing, drawing, or sculpting. In order to process the loss of his alcoholic father, one man I knew went with his therapist to a recycling plant where he could throw bottles and watch the glass explode. Remember, grief often involves sadness and anger.

Trust and believe. Even though you are sure you will never get through this time, you will. Even though you remember your loved one sick or in pain, there will come a day when you will remember the good times. Even though you can't remember what your loved one looked or sounded like, those good memories will come back.

God wants to embrace you in your grief. God is no stranger to grief, having lost his son. Psalm 46 says that God is our refuge. You may struggle with the question *Where was God when my loved one died (or left)?* It's OK to ask God questions. Even Jesus did.

Ultimately, a chapter like this won't bring answers to your questions. And it may not bring comfort. Your loss is devastating. But I hope to remind you that Christians don't grieve like those who have no hope (1 Thessalonians 4:13). Revelation 21:4 reminds us, "He will wipe every tear from their eyes. There will be no more death or mourning or crying or pain, for the old order of things has passed away."

MORE WAYS TO PROCESS YOUR GRIEF

- Allow yourself to have two opposing feelings. Maybe it's love and anger. Perhaps your mom was difficult; that doesn't mean you didn't love her and want her love shown to you.
- Ask a friend or spouse to listen while you talk and cry. Tell him or her not to try to fix it.
- Run. Run and cry.
- Play music loudly and sing and dance. If it's happy music, belt it out. If it's sad, let your tears pour out onto your fake microphone.
- A cool shower or warm bath can help change your brain waves when you feel upset.

- Cook. Chopping vegetables and kneading bread are both very therapeutic.
- Go to a sporting event where it's acceptable to scream. Screaming is a good outlet.
- Read a brainless novel and go to sleep early.
- Allow yourself not to do much. When my dad died it was difficult even to drive to the grocery store. It helped when a friend reminded me of how much emotional space was being taken up by grief.
- Instead of swallowing and stopping tears, let them come—even exaggerate them. Tears remove stress-induced toxic chemicals from the body. They also contain beta-endorphin, one of the body's natural pain relievers.
- Grief has tentacles. Don't be surprised if you start grieving one thing and it attaches to former losses. This is why it is so important to grieve events as you move through life.
- If there is physical injury, it can make grief worse. And vice versa: grief can heighten physical pain. Take extra care of yourself if you are grieving and physically injured or in physical pain.
- Realize guilt is a natural part of grieving. Our society doesn't teach us how to do it well.
- Write a letter to your loved one. You don't have to send it. Tell him or her the good and the bad.
- Light candles.
- Play soothing music.
- Say no to extra commitments.
- Take a walk alone.
- Nap in a sunbeam.

- Get a massage.
- Make love.
- Burn your list of "shoulds."
- Snuggle.
- Limit your news intake.
- Pray.
- Eat healthy food.
- Say kind things to yourself such as, "I will get through this," "I have lived through something excruciating," or, "I gave my loved one all he (or she) needed."

'Tis a fearful thing
To love
What death can touch.
To love, to hope, to dream,
And oh, to lose.
A thing for fools, this,
Love,
But a holy thing,
To love what death can touch.

For your life has lived in me;
Your laugh once lifted me;
Your word was a gift to me.

To remember this brings painful joy.

'Tis a human thing, love,
A holy thing,
To love
What death can touch.
[attributed to Judah Halevi]

In the next chapter, we will look at the role and importance of counseling in our self-care.

CHAPTER 12

RENEWED THROUGH COUNSELING

Pretending that life is easier and more blessed than it really is hinders our ability to walk with God and share him with others. Faith is not the same thing as denial.

—JOHN ELDREDGE

KARLA IS A BLONDE-HAIRED Snow White, sweet beyond belief. But she has experienced an enormous amount of loss over the past ten years. First her mother died. A few years later, following a bout with severe depression, her sister passed away. Around the same time, a painful church split resulted in some of Karla's best friends leaving the church. Further, Karla was hospitalized because of health issues. To top off this painful list of events, her youngest son left for college. Though it was a happy occasion for her son, for Karla it was one too many losses in too short a time. Karla's zeal for life trickled out. She continued to trust that God would heal her. In a conversation with Karla, we talked about my book. "I can see why you wrote it," she said, "and I'm grateful God let psychology help you; but God could still heal me in an instant if he wanted to." Despite obvious depression, Karla has yet to reach out for counseling, waiting for God to heal her.

Ginger clings to her faith. She has Scriptures written on sticky notes stuck to the refrigerator door: "I can do all things through Christ who strengthens me" (Philippians 4:13 NKJV), and, "There is therefore now no condemnation for those who are in Christ Jesus" (Romans 8:1 NRSV). Yet as much as she wants to believe, Ginger cannot get rid of the shame of her past. Recently she broke down and told me that she deserves a bad marriage because of her abortion many years ago.

Bob, a blue-collar man in his sixties, mumbled when he overheard his wife Tina talking to me about antidepressant medications and counseling. "Shrinks are just quacks—she doesn't need any of that mumbo jumbo," he said. Tina decided to wait and talk to me later.

Pastor Frank told the congregation, "You don't need counseling; you just need the Holy Spirit." I thought about all the people who were stuck in emotional pain, leaning on their faith alone, not realizing that faith offered so many resources for healing, even as they continued to pray for their pain to go away. It was puzzling that Pastor Frank felt he needed to say something to his church that he didn't actually believe, since he has seen a counselor in the past and currently attends group therapy.

Roberta's eyes narrowed as she quietly whispered to me, "Why would you go back to school to study psychology?" In her opinion, being a Christian and studying psychology did not belong together. She reminded me about Lisa, a young member of our church who had "gone off to become a counselor" and subsequently got divorced. "That's what psychology did for her," Roberta said.

Each of these confusing reactions to Christian counseling are situations I have encountered (though I have changed the names). Even though some Christians would question that God desires our happiness, most Christians believe that God wants us to have some measure of healing in our lives. Verses such as 1 Peter 4:10, Ephesians 4:16, and Lamentations 3:40 remind us that God has ordained that we examine our ways, grow, and be strengthened in our relationships. Jeremiah 6:14 tells us we can't heal a wound by pretending it's not there or by offering superficial treatments. A quick glance at Scripture assures us that God desires us to have freedom, joy, peace, and healing at some level.

WE ARE HEALED IN RELATIONSHIP

Before my graduate studies, I tried ferociously to move along the path of Christian growth. Now I understand that I had no place to work through the pain of my past, and therefore no place to gain a foothold in understanding why I had engaged in such destructive behaviors that held me in shame.

I had believed a message that in simplified terms taught that accepting Jesus and reading some well-meaning Scriptures were all I needed to enjoy a peaceful life. Now I understand why I couldn't get more healing from a book, lecture, Bible study, or prayer: it is in *relationship* that we incur our greatest wounds, and it must be in *relationship* that we heal them.

The church does not always allow people a safe place to reveal their sinful nature, to understand it, and to heal from it (of course, we will never be fully free this side of heaven). When I finished my graduate program, I was upset that I had been stuck in anxiety, shame, and depression for more than a decade after becoming a devout follower of Christ, only to find healing so immediately in the world of clinical counseling.

I meet so many Christians who are afraid of feelings, who think that if they simply serve the Lord enough, in return God will heal their hurts. People can sit and study their Bible, pray and have faith that God will bring healing—and that sometimes may happen—but most often repair comes within relationships. Dr. Henry Cloud says, "Without a solid, bonded relationship, the human soul will become mired in psychological and emotional problems. The soul cannot prosper without being connected to others" (*Changes That Heal*, 47). I would add one word to Cloud's sentence: the soul cannot prosper without being intimately connected to others. That kind of intimacy doesn't happen simply by attending church, working in ministry, singing hymns, and memorizing Scripture. It comes by being authentic and by taking risks to open up with trusted people.

Though the Christian self-help bookshelf is saturated with books telling Christians how to heal from emotional wounds, almost all of them rely on spirituality solely, rather than on psychology. Spirituality and healthy psychology work in tandem as gifts from God. This is the reason I started writing this book. There are so many people stuck in their pain because they keep hoping the next spiritual truth or Bible study will heal their emotional hurts.

Though I still didn't know the extent of my own wounds, or the way to heal them, I somehow understood that my degree in counseling psychology would be helpful. I had no idea that there were people opposed to the idea of psychology working in the midst of a life of faith.

Science has been useful to Christians in many arenas—astronomy, medicine, mathematics, botany, and so on—so why wouldn't science be useful to Christians in the arena of thinking and behavior? Imagine if you dropped a cinder block on your foot. You wouldn't sit in your room, clinging to faith and prayer, hoping your foot would be healed. You would get up and go see a doctor. Why is it different with emotional wounds? Often we are lead to believe that we can heal from emotional wounds simply by having faith and praying. Because I believe so much healing happens within a counselor's office, I see that God has given us tools, wisdom, knowledge, and skilled clinicians to aid in the process of healing.

OUR EMOTIONAL HEALTH AFFECTS OUR PHYSICAL HEALTH

No one argues with the idea that emotional symptoms often affect our bodies in physical ways—our negative emotions can cause disease. When Dr. Michael Crichton (author of *Jurassic Park*) surveyed heart-attack patients, he asked them, "Why did you have this heart attack?" All gave an answer based on emotion: "I hated my job," or, "I was mad at my son." People suffering from depression tend to experience more severe and long-lasting physical pain than other people because the nervous system interacts with other parts of the body. The overlap of anxiety, depression, and pain is evidenced in conditions such as fibromyalgia, irritable bowel syndrome, lower back pain, headaches, and nerve pain.

If this describes you, take heart. It is never too late to begin the healing process that can turn your life around. Brain science reveals that depression, high stress, and childhood trauma change people's brains. Dr. Norman Doidge says the hippocampus of depressed adults who suffered childhood trauma can be up to 18 percent smaller. If stress is brief, the decrease in size is temporary. If it is prolonged, the damage is permanent. Glucocorticoids are released, and cells are killed in the hippocampus, leading to memory loss. As people recover from depression, their hippocampi can grow back and memories return. Brain studies show that antidepressant medications, as well as counseling, can increase the number of stem cells in the hippocampus. By using medications that foster neuronal growth, we may be helping people improve brain flexibility and memory (*The Brain that Changes Itself*, 241).

EXPRESSING EMOTIONS AND TELLING OUR STORIES

Parents who have not learned to express their own emotions often have trouble letting their children cry; they don't let them feel sad, mad, or even joyful. They say things like, "Stop crying or I'll give you something to cry about." Sometimes it's subtler. One day my son and I were taking a drive, and he was discouraged about something. I caught myself telling him to cheer up, but then realized it was healthy for him to express his sadness. He was simply feeling the freedom to release his emotions. Of course, there are right and wrong ways for expressing those emotions, and this is where healthier parenting and modeling comes in.

Emotional garbage buried in the trash compactor of our souls always finds a way out. I've heard several phrases that capture what unprocessed emotion does: "Grief waits"; "Either you work it out or you act it out"; and, "The bill always presents itself." When I went to college I had no model for how to deal with my mother's recent death, so I went into "bury the garbage" mode—carrying on as if nothing had happened, acting happy while using drugs, alcohol, and sex to quench the hurt. John Powell, the famous theologian, says, "If you bury a feeling, you bury it alive." This is exactly what happens.

Looking back, I realize that I had tried for years to tell my story to friends and pastors with whom I had surrounded myself. Unknowingly, they interrupted my process by giving me the message, "But you have a life of faith, now. That changes everything."

What I know now is that owning our stories can be difficult, but not as difficult as alienating ourselves from them. The cure for shame is looking someone in the eye and telling him or her what causes your shame. A mentor in the counseling program did this for me. Poet John Fox describes it well in his poem "When Someone Deeply Listens To You." In his poem, Fox describes holding a dented childhood cup. As you watch, the cup becomes filled with refreshing water. As the water rises to the top and stops, you are understood. However, Fox says, "When it overflows and touches your skin, / you are loved."

I am convinced that God wants to use our stories for God's glory. Just as the ancient Hebrews of the Bible took plunder with them when they left their bondage in Egypt—a plunder later used to build God's tabernacle—emotionally healed Christians get to use their stories to help others and glorify God.

Many churches infamously disregard the need to create space for people to reveal their emotional wounds. Instead, many in the church are quick to condemn poor behavior, without taking the time to understand why someone is prone to cheat, use drugs, gamble, starve, binge, or self-injure.

A key practice I learned in school was always to ask the client where he or she is, though not necessarily using those specific words. God asked Adam after the fall, "Where are you?" Of course God knew where Adam was, but he wanted to hear Adam's own description and perception of his predicament. In telling his story, Adam would return to relationship with God and others, albeit imperfectly.

Sometimes church leaders put people in a box with a label instead of hearing what individual journeys in life have been like. What are the stories of hurt, abuse, neglect, or trauma that are behind the more visible story of addiction or anger? Some of us remain stuck in a silent hell without a safe place within the church to tell our true stories. Pity the soul who has a bipolar disorder and is told to have more faith and pray harder, when lithium derived from salts in the earth's soil could allow him to live a normal life. Even the Apostle Paul didn't tell Timothy to pray harder and have more faith, but told him to take a little wine for his stomach issues (1 Timothy 5:23).

TRAUMAS FROM OUR PAST

Dan Allender, in his highly acclaimed book *The Wounded Heart*, echoes my experience of emotionally wounded Christians who haven't uncovered their stories: "The first great enemy to lasting change is the propensity to turn our eyes away from the wound and pretend things are fine." He says:

> After a time, however, the unclaimed pain of the past presses for resolution, and the only solution is to continue to deny. The result is either a sense of deep personal contempt for one's inability to forgive and forget, or a deepened sense of betrayal toward those who desired to silence the pain. . . . *Hiding the past always involves denial; denial of the past is always a denial of God.* (14–15)

We bring into adulthood some of the ways we get wounded as children, including our deficits and our denial about these wounds. Some of these events may be so commonplace that we minimize the impact.

Essentially, trauma results from an event that you are unable to make sense out of. Below are some events that can cause wounding.

Divorce. An Oprah Winfrey show featured a rabbi teaching

the audience ways to help children survive divorce with minimal damage. Oprah was flooded with messages from viewers in their forties, fifties, and sixties still crippled by their parents' divorces. This prompted Oprah to do another show for these older "children." Just because divorce is common doesn't mean the impact is benign. In addition to grief and loss, divorce prevents children from having a template of what a successful marriage looks like; it is no secret that children who come from divorced homes suffer higher rates of divorce themselves.

Post-traumatic Stress Disorder (PTSD). PTSD is a disorder following exposure to an overwhelming trauma usually involving threat of injury, death, or threat to self, and always involving feelings of extreme helplessness. PTSD is followed by symptoms of persistent mental reexperiencing of the event (or feelings associated with it), avoidance of anything remotely associated with the trauma, and hyperarousal of the autonomic nervous system. Even though PTSD is generally a diagnosis for those who have experienced overwhelming stressors in life, even smaller traumas, such as being teased in school, can leave highly sensitive people so ashamed and hurt that they, too, exhibit PTSD symptoms. Traumatized individuals feel stuck in a no-win situation: on the one hand, painful memories are vying to be reprocessed; on the other hand, the individual wants to avoid thinking about the event. For anyone considering counseling, be assured that experts in PTSD counseling will never take you beyond your comfort zone, and will work with you so that you will always feel safe. Part of the "cure" for helping process the memories is to process them in the company of understanding and soothing safety, rather than continue to deal with them alone or ignore them altogether.

A factor that goes hand in hand with PTSD is substance abuse. As traumatic memories attempt to make their presence known, there is a huge desire within affected people to quell inner anxiety. This is where the attempt to numb with alcohol or other substances comes in. As a clinician, I believe that the opposite of addiction is "exposure therapy" through counseling. Helping people process their trauma helps them lose the need to numb with substances.

Complex Post-traumatic Stress Disorder. Complex PTSD is a fairly new label given to people who have incurred a lifetime of trauma—from neglect to emotional abuse, from witnessing repetitive arguments to enduring physical and sexual abuse. The impact of childhood neglect, violence, and emotional abuse can haunt people for decades, long after their abuser is gone.

Though there is an ongoing debate about spanking, the effects of corporal punishment can leave deep emotional scars. Many researchers have found corporal punishment to be extremely ineffective for stopping unwanted behavior, even if it stops the behavior for the short term. It can create generalized fear towards caregivers, and the offending behavior often returns. Research shows that removing a positive reward such as playtime or a cell phone—depending on age—is a more effective means of stopping an unwanted behavior. Some parents repeat the pattern of spanking because they learned it from their parents or because they have been taught it is "God's way of discipline." If you could sit in the counselor's chair, you'd cringe at how many Scriptures have been taken out of context in toxic religious environments to support everything from belittling to beating.

Childhood Sexual Abuse. As I reported earlier, statistics show that one in three women and one in six men have been sexually abused before the age of eighteen. The numbers are likely higher, making childhood sexual abuse epidemic. Sexual abuse includes incest, sexual molestation, rape, sodomy, exhibitionism, and other acts of sexual exploitation carried out toward a child. Such abuse may be nonphysical, such as obscene phone calls or indecent exposure, or exposure to pornography for the purpose of another's gratification. The effects of childhood sexual abuse can include low self-esteem, shame, fear of intimacy, lack of trust, self-injurious behavior, suicide, substance abuse, emotional mood swings, depression, anxiety, promiscuity or sexual addiction, and poor boundaries.

Depression and Anxiety. Sometimes people don't even know they are depressed or anxious. Because they've always felt a certain way, they don't understand that they could feel better. They may not feel the lowest lows, but they also don't feel the highest highs. They don't let loose a belly laugh or act spontaneously. Many clients experience true happiness, new to them, after working through their wounds in therapy.

Parents who suffer from depression and anxiety sometimes can pass these symptoms on to their children. Although some people assume their depression and anxiety is hereditary, passed down through the genes, for the most part anxiety and depression are passed on to children through parenting practices and modeling. When one generation stops the pattern and heals, it positively affects generations to come. Taking time out to heal your brain and body is one of the most unselfish things you can do for yourself, your children, and your grandchildren.

Alcoholism or Substance Abuse. Children raised in alcoholic homes are more likely to have anxiety, depression, antisocial behavior, relationship difficulties, behavioral problems, and substance abuse. Children believe the world revolves around them. Because of this, children assume they cause bad things, and may assume their parent's drinking and subsequent behavior happens because of them. Many children of alcoholics suffer shame, fear, and tension. They may experience chaos, instability, inconsistent discipline, emotional and physical neglect, physical or sexual abuse, and loneliness; and they are often forced to witness violence. They learn to deny reality and their own emotions, and they learn unspoken rules such as "don't talk, trust, or tell." Among the most devastating issues for children of alcoholics is the failure to develop their own ego, or sense of self, because of constant attention paid to other cues within the home. Alcoholic homes are often violent homes. Studies have found that witnessing violence is as damaging to a child as experiencing it firsthand. Children of alcoholics also often become perfectionists, trying to keep up appearances that all is normal. And they tend to be caretakers of others to a fault—that is, in codependency.

Loss or Death. Loss is a natural part of life, and we've all experienced it to one degree or another. Even something as simple as being an only child and then being pushed out of the "baby" position when another child is born in the family can be traumatic.

There are so many other ways that children become emotionally wounded adults. Children of those with illness, disease, or mental illness—all of which can affect the developing child—can become emotionally wounded adults. I recently learned about an interesting study that investigated the link between childhood maltreatment and later-life health and well-being. The study examined eight adverse childhood experiences (ACEs):

1. emotional abuse
2. physical abuse
3. sexual abuse
4. battered mother
5. parental separation or divorce
6. substance-abusing mother
7. mentally ill mother
8. incarcerated household member

The Centers for Disease Control and Prevention and Kaiser Permanente's Health Appraisal Clinic in San Diego collaborated on the study. More than seventeen thousand members participated, and more than thirty further scientific studies have been done with the data.

Almost two-thirds of participants reported at least one ACE, and more than one in five reported three or more ACEs. Childhood abuse, neglect, and exposure to other traumatic stressors are associated with increases in alcohol abuse, chronic obstructive pulmonary disease (COPD), depression, and a whole host of other health risks and adverse behaviors.

Most of us have some level of work we need to do to renew ourselves and to renew and protect children within our care or our extended families. When we seek to renew ourselves with counseling for these or other issues, we move through and past blaming abusers, getting back at neglectful parents, or laying burdens at the feet of other humans who can't change our pasts. Counseling helps us deal with the pain of dysfunction and put a stop to multigenerational illnesses that plague our families.

In tandem with prayer, and the guidance and wisdom of Scripture, we can work with the intervention of a trained counselor to help guide our wounded souls through the struggle of emotional healing, rather than getting stuck waiting for a miracle. We can begin that miracle work now. A combination of counseling, relaxation training, exercise, antidepressants, and mood stabilizers may offer people significant relief.

In the next chapter, we will consider the importance of connection in self-care.

CHAPTER 13

RENEWED
THROUGH
CONNECTION

*If there ever comes a day when we can't
be together, keep me in your heart, I'll
stay there forever.*

— WINNIE THE POOH

IN 1995 THE FORT WORTH Star-Telegram
assigned journalist Tim Madigan the task of writing about children's television icon Fred Rogers
(*Mister Rogers' Neighborhood*). In the book *I'm Proud of
You*, Tim describes the unexpected and healing bond the
two men formed. When the friendship began, Tim was a
depressed man. He and his wife were on the verge of

divorce. He could not escape depression, which he called "the furies." Through letters and phone calls Tim began to understand that his emotional state was rooted in the fact that his father had never been able to share how proud he was of Tim. Fred Rogers became a surrogate father, letting Tim know how proud he was of him. Surrounded by the love of one man, Tim learned to cry and be honest about his feelings. This openness began the work of alleviating his depression and healing family wounds. Tim's marriage healed and his family blossomed.

For the first few years of my counseling practice I read—and believed—a lot of books that taught that the way to mental health was to pull away from others and to have a clear sense of self. If there were relational problems, it just meant you were too connected—enmeshed—and needed to pull back. Some counselors call this "differentiation." My thinking has now changed. Having a sense of identity is important, but connection with others is also essential to self-care and happiness. All happiness research points to connectedness as the vital aspect. Maintaining a healthy sense of belonging and attachment is critical. Why people feel and act the way they do lies in the profound effect of a child's bonding process with his or her caregivers early on.

One of the most frequent problems I see in my counseling office is people who are afraid to be seen. They tell me how they want to slither into the cracks of my couch. They wish to disappear through eating disorders, through being perfectly pleasant, or by hiding all emotion. They smile and tell me they are fine, but their body language conveys a different truth. They want to be invisible: in their family of origin,

showing up meant getting hit or sexually violated or emotionally leaned on by adults. Juvenile brains aren't equipped
to deal with adult problems. Being invisible keeps people
unconnected. Whereas this may have been a tool to help
someone survive childhood, sooner or later loneliness takes
root. Human beings are not meant to be alone.

CONNECTION STARTS EARLY

When parents attend to their youngsters' needs, children
gain the ability to self-soothe—they learn to calm themselves
after experiencing life's ups and downs. They also achieve
something psychologists call "emotional object constancy,"
which means they are able to experience themselves as
loved, even in the absence of loved ones. That's because the
loved one is internalized. Children can go out into the world
successfully because, in a sense, Mom and Dad are inside
them. Important research now points to attachment theory
as a major factor in marriage research: partners who did not
securely attach to parental figures in childhood struggle to
attach to each other in adulthood. How successfully children
form and maintain relationships throughout life is related to
those early bonds of attachment. Attachment theory states
that everyone has a relationship style that will show up,
especially during times of stress and duress. There are four
basic attachment styles associated with certain characteristic
patterns of behavior:

1. *Avoidant.* This person has an overinflated view of self
   and a poor view of others. Maybe as a child he had a

depressed mother, or maybe he was a colicky baby. If his mother didn't respond, he learned to rely on himself for soothing. He learned to turn toward things for comfort. Perhaps addiction is sewn early into a child's life.

2. *Ambivalent.* This person has a poor view of self and an overinflated view of others. She constantly seeks approval. Ambivalent people are typically the worker bees in a ministry, church, or family, but eventually they become exhausted trying to win affection from others.

3. *Disorganized.* This person grew up with trauma. He has a poor view of self and of others. He can't turn to himself or others for comfort.

4. *Secure.* This person has a healthy view of self and of others. She sees her good and bad traits, and she can turn toward others without idealizing or fearing them.

Every day you are asking this question of yourself and others: "Are you trustworthy, accessible, and capable of loving me?" The answer you tell yourself not only influences your relationships with others but also your relationship with God. (Among the terrific books that address this are *Hold Me Tight* by Sue Johnson, *Attachments* by Gary Sibcy and Tim Clinton, and *How We Love* by Milan Yerkovich.)

CREATED FOR RELATIONSHIP

Because God created us for relationship, relationship has a profound influence on our lives. Consider the Trinity. The Trinity—Father, Son, and Holy Spirit—reflects the social nature of God as three in one. God made angels and humans, again bringing creatures into social orientation. In Genesis 3, God said everything was good—and only called one thing not good: for man to be alone. Even the Old Testament word *Azar* (*'ezer, 'ezra*), often used to refer to God, means to come alongside, to protect, to support.

Even from a very young age, being included seems to be hardwired into our nature. Studies show that the same areas of the brain are affected when we are excluded as when we experience physical pain. Social isolation, not surprisingly, is as big a risk factor as smoking, and people with nonexistent or very small social circles are at greater risk for cognitive decline and memory loss. Some of us think we can get by with our pull-yourself-up-by-your-bootstraps mentality, but try doing that long enough and you'll realize it's not very effective. Sure, it keeps us protected but it keeps us alone.

In recent years I have trained in a model of marriage therapy called Emotionally Focused Therapy (EFT). This model was developed by Sue Johnson and is based on attachment theory, which has as its premise the idea that people need to be attached and attuned to a safe "other" in order to branch out into the world. When marriages struggle, EFT therapists focus on people not knowing how to turn toward each other and ask from a vulnerable place for their needs to be met. They don't know how to say, "I'm scared when you talk to that other woman," or, "When you yell at me like that, I feel like I can't meet your needs. I feel like I'm not a good man." Instead, couples either pursue or distance—screaming and demanding for their needs to be met, or pulling away in fear of not being enough. This creates a dance that eventually turns into a toxic misstep. A pursuer may think that she told her mate how much she needs him, but she does not do it in a vulnerable way that comes from her core needs (for example, fear, sadness, or longing). She verbally attacks. And the withdrawer may think that he has told his mate that he's scared he can't meet her needs, but all she senses is his pulling away again. Consider for a moment how you learned to feel safe and get your needs met as a child.

Those who've suffered violations of human connection in previous relationships find it difficult to learn to trust and to rely on others later in life. Secure attachment is the natural antidote to traumatic experiences. In fact, the best predictor of who will thrive after a traumatic experience are those who can seek out attachment with others and who are able to find people who will respond with comfort. Think about what you did after 9/11 or any other tragedy. Most people rushed to get close to the ones they love.

EMOTIONAL CONNECTION AND SEXUAL INTIMACY

Neural network wires get tangled when people have trauma, and emotional intimacy may become mixed up with sexual intimacy. People longing for emotional connection sometimes erroneously medicate with large quantities of sex. Sexual addiction is not just limited to men, and for both male and female addicts it is not really about the sex. Sexual addiction is really a fear of emotional intimacy. Sex is used as medicine to take way the panicky feelings a sex addict feels. It's a way for a person to feel empowered and comforted.

However, the sex doesn't take away the emotional pain for

very long. Sexual addiction (like all addictions) is a way to numb emotional pain. Sex addicts have a lot of ambivalence: there is a craving for closeness, but at the same time there is a fear of it. This is because the very ones who caused a sex addict's emotional wounds were those closest to him or her. These wounded men and women seek sexual closeness, and they idealize the encounter into an "all good" event; but at the same time, it's scary to get emotionally close to others.

A woman with love and sex addiction who cares about renewal should find a therapist who is comfortable talking about this issue (understandably, seeing a male or female counselor will bring up different types of longing and safety issues for the client, therefore it is paramount that the counselor has skill, boundaries, and integrity). She needs someone who understands how a person's brain wiring confuses a desire for emotional closeness with a sexual encounter used to settle anxiety and numb her pain. She needs someone who sees her underlying hurts and helps her tell her story. Long before a woman sexualizes her pain, there is sadness and longing in her life. She may have to create a healthy bond with a counselor before she is able to reach out to others.

One of the most important lessons I ever learned about connection with others occurred when I was at an intensive healing workshop. In one exercise, our group was told to walk blindfolded through a maze while holding onto a rope. We were also given three pieces of instruction:

1. There is a way out.
2. Don't let go of the rope.
3. If you can't figure it out, ask for help.

I remember how crazy I felt when I bumped into others and felt them back up, clearly at a dead end made out of chairs and pylons. I felt them wander away. I heard groans of frustration, and then a lot of laughter as people figured it out. As I heard more people get out, I got angrier and more desperate. Fiercely I moved along, groping madly. I was going to figure it out—I was! With a blindfold over my eyes and tears streaming down my face, I finally stopped struggling. I shot my hand toward the ceiling. A voice whispered, "Yes?"

"I can't do this! Will you help?" I cried.

As the woman removed the blindfold from my face, she commented, "That's the answer." You see, there was no way out—crying out for help was the answer. All the rope lines led to roadblocks. The lesson: people need one another, but sometimes we have to learn the hard way.

CONNECTION WITH OTHER WOMEN

Women especially need connection with other women. Scientists call this behavioral pattern "tend and befriend." We know that when under stress people react with fight or flight. But newer research shows that females are less likely to respond with fear-related behavior and physical aggression. Instead, they do lunch. They get together to talk and touch. Oxytocin and endorphins are released, and the stressed brain calms when positive social contact is made. In addition to calming the brain, friends help us think through problems, consider solutions, and maintain objectivity. The happiest people are those who learn how to reveal themselves and create safe relationships with others.

TIPS FOR CONNECTING

- Realize that no one is perfect. Some people search for passion that never fades, and use this as an excuse not to commit. But unrealistic infatuation is really just a bunch of hormones that surge through the body. They always dissipate by about eighteen months. Real love, a quieter thing, is what is left.

- Be a good listener. It's amazing how much people love to talk about themselves. I've never forgotten Dale Carnegie's advice: "People like you based on how you make them feel." Notice I didn't say that they like you based on your looks, your clothes, your job, and your achievements. They like you based on how you make them feel. When you let people talk about themselves, they are going to feel good about themselves. They will feel like they were interesting, and they will like you.

- Ask for help before you get into crises. Let go of shame, pride, and embarrassment. Everyone needs help. It doesn't mean you are inadequate. If you're afraid to ask for help, talk to a close friend. Maybe she or he could help you see what you're not seeing, or help you role-play who and how to ask for more help.

- Tell people what you need. State clearly what you need, and stay positive. Avoid being whiney or vague. Most people would love to help; they just don't know how.

Remember to say thank you. Respect someone's no, and ask someone else who can help.

- If you are someone who equates emotional intimacy with sex, practice getting your needs met through talking and nonsexual touch. For some, this is difficult. If this is an area of wounding and concern, consider addressing the deeper issues through counseling.

- Men and women tend to define intimacy differently. Men are more likely to say they had an intimate time doing an activity, whereas women are more likely to say they experienced emotional intimacy when they were talking. When you're with your mate, consider spending time doing both: a hike and a talk; a drive and a talk.

- If you don't have a church, find one—even if you're skeptical or haven't been in a long time. Being in community with a group of people is good for the soul. Studies show that having one place where you're expected to show up even one time a month has the same happiness impact as doubling your income. I call this the *Cheers* effect.

- Instead of being nice, practice being who you are. I love what Dr. Phil says about relationships: "We need to invest in a relationship, but if being half of a couple means you have to stop being all of who you are, the price is too high." (If kicking him or her out leaves you emotionally bankrupt, then you haven't taken care of who you are).

- Consider forming a tribe or taking a class. Try book clubs, random acts of kindness clubs, or clubs to help the elderly or parents of sick children. I know a woman who gets together with friends every month to explore one cultural experience. My yoga class started a book club, and we do a cookie exchange at Christmas. I routinely get together with my friends to take photographs or classes.

- Don't compare. Realize that we tend to overestimate how happy other people are. When people post happy events on social media, women are especially vulnerable to thinking their lives don't measure up.
- Don't wait for someone to reach out to you. Pick up the phone or e-mail a friend and ask to get together.

In the next and final chapter, we will focus on generosity and gratitude as powerful tools of self-care.

CHAPTER 14

RENEWED THROUGH GENEROSITY AND GRATITUDE

A thankful heart is not only the greatest virtue, but the parent to all the other virtues.

— CICERO

MY DAUGHTER AND I TOOK the escalator down one level at the train station in Liege, Belgium. We were making a transfer from the train we boarded in Maastricht (in The Netherlands) to the one that would take us into Brussels. As we vied for our space near the yellow line and the train approached, I glanced at a mother and adolescent daughter wrapped in black coats. Squeezing on board and glancing around, I noticed two empty seats next to the women I had seen earlier.

As we sat next to them, Taylor and I chatted about our adventures. She had spent a college semester abroad, and I had joined her for the tail end of her journey; the two of us were now traveling together. The girl next to me held a tattered dictionary from which she would sound out words and spell them for her mother. Intrigued, I began to ask about their lives. They were homeless from the collapse of the Soviet Union in 1991. They had fled to a Belgium refugee camp after the girl's father was murdered and their home was burned. The mother and daughter shared their story with hope that they were making a better life. They were using the once-a-month free train pass that the refugee camp provided them with, in order to shop at a flea market. Even though they didn't show self-pity, tears began to stream down my face. Taylor looked at me with a mixture of embarrassment and empathy.

As the intercom announced our stop, I grabbed all the cash in my wallet and asked, "Please, may I give this to you?" They shook their heads, and their cheeks turned red. "It is not a hardship. It will bless us. Please let us give this to you," I implored. By then all four of us were weeping. Quickly I asked if I could take their pictures and continue to pray for them. They pulled our wet faces to theirs and kissed us, saying, "Lucille and Taylor, we will pray for you. Thank you, thank you." When Taylor and I got off the train and walked into Brussels for our sightseeing, we both agreed that we wished we had more money to give them.

In the months since, we have been able to e-mail back and forth, and never once have they asked for more money. Currently, the daughter and her sister have passed very difficult exams and have learned to speak two languages fluently. They are now studying at a university.

I share this story to remind myself (and you) of the magnificent feeling we all get when we can meet a need. Generosity changed us. Taylor and I bonded with these women in a way neither of us will probably ever experience again, and I am finding it difficult to even describe the intense love we seemed to feel in our brief time together.

In fact, neurobiological research shows that people who volunteer activate the same frontal regions of the brain that are activated by awe, wonder, and transcendence. Dopamine and serotonin, the body's feel-good chemicals, are released from these cortical and limbic parts of the brain.

Philosophers as far back as the ancient Greeks and Romans claimed gratitude as an indispensable virtue, but current scientific research can actually measure and record the benefits of generosity, gratitude, volunteerism, and optimism.

GENEROSITY AND GRATITUDE

Current happiness research confirms that there are certain universal traits linked to happiness, and generosity always appears near the top of the list. Most people find great meaning in showing concern for others—it seems to be a universal desire to reduce the suffering of others and to improve their lives. In fact, one study in which people did a random act of kindness that involved something as small as a five-dollar bill found it was enough to make the giver happy. It also caused the immune system to improve and depression levels to decrease in the giver.

You can plan to do acts of kindness for others. Here is a list of ideas to get you started.

- Create May Day baskets.
- Look for ways to give away five dollars or twenty dollars.
- Pay the toll for the driver behind you.
- Secretly buy the pizza for the teens next to your table.
- Hold a door and smile at someone.
- Hug a friend.
- Smile at a stranger. It costs you nothing and usually makes an impact on them.
- Shovel a neighbor's snowy driveway.
- Put your neighbor's newspaper on his or her doorstep.
- Leave change in the soda machine.
- Take a meal to a family in need.
- Drop off disposable diapers or food to a community resource bank.
- Offer one of your sick days to someone who doesn't have any left.

Interestingly, there seems to be a connection between gratitude and generosity. People who experience generosity and feel grateful want to repay those who have given to them, as well as extend it to third parties—they want to pay it forward. The word *gratitude* originates from the Latin word *gratia*, from which we get words such as *grace, graciousness*, and *gratefulness*. It means, "thankfulness, appreciation, or kindness." With gratitude, you acknowledge the good in your life. As you do this, you recognize that the source of this good lies at least partially outside yourself; therefore, gratitude helps you connect to something larger than self, be it nature, others, or God. Gratitude helps people feel positive emotions, improve their health, savor good experiences, and build strong relationships.

Odd as it may seem, the times surrounding my father's death highlighted my sense of gratitude. It was a long unexpected journey—things went bad after a routine hernia surgery. I lived in a hotel for twelve days because my father lived in another town. During that time, I experienced many random acts of kindness that may have seemed small but touched me in a powerful way. I've come to believe that during the crisis, kind acts and my ensuing gratitude were magnified.

Friends randomly texted throughout the day: "You're on my mind. God is using you. I'm praying for you!" The hotel staff where I was staying put two handwritten cards in my room: "We're so sorry you are here for medical reasons. We hope you have a comfortable stay in our hotel." This touched me more than I can express, and it made me a devout customer of that hotel chain. My cousins showed up at the hospital each day, just to be there alongside me. They took my siblings and me out to lunch, and refused to let us pay. I wanted to read Scripture to my dad, but I didn't have a Bible. However, I did have my phone, so I asked friends on Facebook to post the most comforting Scriptures they knew. I was able to scroll with one hand and hold my dad's with the other. Several times, he moaned the words, "Thank you."

Because my dad refused further medical treatment—and made that clear to everyone around him—it became his children's wishes to honor that. But at times, it felt like we were being cruel for allowing him this choice. Several of my friends e-mailed to tell me how proud of me they were. This was validating. It told me that they understood how difficult this was, and it gave me courage to continue. Before going through this, I would not have known that telling someone, "I'm proud of you," would be such a helpful thing to hear.

The power of prayer cannot be underestimated. I knew my friends were praying, and I truly believe that is what sustained me.

GRATITUDE AND HAPPINESS

Gratitude, hope, vitality, curiosity, and love—Harvard research has found these virtues strongly and consistently are linked to happiness. That kindness, or gift, need not be tangible. It could be a simple gesture or intent that is represented rather than the actual item or benefit given. Maybe you offer to drive a friend home from the car mechanic's shop, but instead she chooses the time to sit there and read. The unused offer still carries meaning to both involved. One study found three distinct aspects of gratitude:

1. A warm sense of appreciation for something or somebody
2. A sense of goodwill toward that thing or person
3. A resulting disposition to act positively

Gratitude is the key to happiness, and happiness seems to make good things happen. The benefits of happiness may include higher income, superior work outcomes, larger social rewards such as longer marriages and more friends, more activity, increased energy, better physical health, and longer life. Happy people are more creative, helpful, charitable, and self-confident; have better self-control; and show greater self-regulatory and coping abilities. Happiness can add as many as nine years to your life because happiness is a quality of renewal.

In one study led by Dr. Robert Emmons and Mike McCullough, subjects were divided into three groups. The first group described five things they were thankful for; the second group wrote about five daily hassles; and the third group wrote about things that had affected them, but they were not told whether to focus on the positive or on the negative. After ten weeks, those who wrote about gratitude were happier and more optimistic. Surprisingly, they also exercised more and had fewer visits to the doctor than those who wrote about hassles.

Another study found that managers who remember to say thank you to their employees may actually motivate them to work harder. Marriage researcher John Gottman's twenty years of research shows that if a couple is unable to maintain a high level (5:1 or greater) ratio of positive encounters (for example, smiles, compliments, laughter, appreciation) to negative encounters (for example, frown, put-down, complaint), the marriage will end. In fact, he can observe a couple for three minutes and determine with 90 percent accuracy whose marriage will flourish and whose will fail.

Can you recall the last time you told someone how much he or she meant to you, how precious your time with him or her was, or how much his or her support enabled you to endure a difficult circumstance? Have you ever tracked down an old acquaintance to thank him or her for making a difference in your life? If so, do you remember how sharing that message made you and the object of your gratitude feel?

Dr. Martin Seligman asked 411 people to write a letter of gratitude to someone alive or dead, someone who had not been properly thanked for his or her kindness. The happiness benefits to the letter writer, and the decrease in his or her depression scores, were greater than any other exercise in Seligman's happiness study—and the benefits lasted for six months!

GRATITUDE AND LONGER, HEALTHIER LIVES

People who are grateful generally live longer lives. In a fascinating longitudinal study, Catholic nuns who expressed gratitude, happiness, and positive emotions in their earlier years were found to live an average of up to ten years longer than their peers who did not express gratitude. Researchers Deborah Danner, David Snowden, and Wallace Friesen discovered a significant inverse relationship between the positive emotional content in handwritten autobiographies of 180 Catholic nuns (at an average age of twenty-two) and the risk of death later in life (ages seventy-five to ninety-five). Expressions of positive emotions such as gratefulness in early life autobiographies seemed to relate to longevity of life sixty years later.

Grateful people report fewer incidences of stress and depression compared to those who focus on neutral or negative aspects of their lives. Researchers have found that when we think about someone or something we love, the parasympathetic—or calming—branch of the autonomic nervous system is activated. When this pattern is repeated, a protective effect is bestowed on the heart: heart rhythm patterns associated with appreciation differ markedly from those associated with relaxation or anger. Negative emotions create a chain in the body where blood vessels constrict and blood pressure rises, and the immune system is weakened. Rather than ruminating over the negative aspects of one's life, those who appreciate and extend gratitude seem to be able to find enjoyment from whatever their current circumstances may be.

Grateful people take better care of themselves and engage in more protective health behaviors, such as regular exercise, a healthy diet, and regular physical examinations. Psychologists theorize that being grateful forces people to overcome what psychologists call "the negativity bias." If you are focused on blessings, you cannot simultaneously focus on anger, greed, envy, or bitterness.

GRATITUDE AND OPTIMISM

A subcategory closely related to gratitude is *optimism*. This isn't the ooey-gooey Pollyanna type of outlook of a person who blindly believes things will always work out. A healthy optimist understands that risks and setbacks are a normal part of life's progress. Dr. Seligman says, "If a setback is thought about as temporary, changeable, and local, that's optimism. If it's thought about as permanent, unchangeable, and pervasive, that's pessimism" (Funderberg, "How to Be an Optimist"). The correlation between gratitude and optimism is important because optimism also has health-related benefits: optimistic individuals report faster recovery and better quality of life after cardiac interventions. Optimism is inversely related to perceived levels of distress and rapid disease progression. There is a direct correlation between optimism and certain situations. For example, optimism can improve the survival rates of persons with HIV as well as those who have some forms of cancer. It can also be beneficial to pregnant women, older adults, and college students adapting to their initial semester. Optimists experience significantly lower risks of fatal cardiovascular events and a reduced risk of death from all causes.

Jeffery Garten, Dean of the Yale School of Management, interviewed forty of the world's most successful business executives, and found they were all optimistic. Seligman's research concludes that optimism can be taught but one must be willing to look for the bright side, even if it means distorting reality a bit. Other factors that determine our optimism level are genetics (50 percent seems to be passed on in our genes. According to Dr. David T. Lykken, each of us has a happiness "set point" that bounces back regardless of good or bad events in our lives); our mother's level of optimism (perhaps this is because mothers do the majority of childrearing); and the reality of events in our lives.

GRATITUDE AND SPIRITUALITY

There appears to be a spiritual quality to gratitude—grateful people have a sense of wonder and humility, and yet they get as much or more in return for giving as the receiver gets from receiving. They somehow recognize their connectedness to others and God, and they cherish the opportunity to pass along gifts to others. Viktor Frankl, a Nazi concentration camp survivor, recognized that everything could be taken from a person and yet he or she could still find meaning (and I suspect gratitude) to be the primary value in life:

> We who lived in concentration camps can remember the men who walked through the huts comforting others, giving away their last piece of bread. They may have been few in number, but they offer sufficient proof that everything can be taken from a man but one thing: the last of the human freedoms—to choose one's attitude in any given set of circumstances, to choose one's own way. (*Man's Search for Meaning*, 65–66)

Another Holocaust survivor, Elie Wiesel, told Oprah Winfrey, "For me, every hour is grace. And I feel gratitude in my heart each time I can meet someone and look at his or her smile."

Another benefit of those who show gratitude is that they tend to stop taking people or their own blessings (fortunate situations) for granted. When we feel grateful for our lives and those around us, we treat others better; we dive into our days with more happiness and energy. In other words, feeling grateful has an exponential effect on our lives—our gratitude makes us more grateful. Here is a wonderful example of gratitude, written by Jane Kenyon, who was suffering from leukemia:

I got out of bed
on two strong legs. It might have been
otherwise. I ate
cereal, sweet
milk, ripe, flawless
peach. It might
have been otherwise.
I took the dog uphill
to the birch wood.
All morning I did
the work I love.

At noon I lay down
with my mate. It might
have been otherwise.
We ate dinner together
at a table with silver
candlesticks. It might
have been otherwise.
I slept in a bed
in a room with paintings
on the walls, and
planned another day
just like this day.
But one day, I know,
it will be otherwise.
[*Collected Poems*, 266]

Years ago, I sent a handwritten thank you note to my eye doctor. I described how professionally he and his staff had treated me. The next time I went in, he had the note taped to the inside of my chart, and he told me how touched he was because so few people take the time to do such a thing. From then on I have received nothing but stellar treatment from him. Of course I didn't write the note with the intention of receiving better treatment. I just remember how good it felt for me to take the time to sincerely thank him. Even the psalms remind us, "It is good to give thanks to the LORD, / And to sing praises to Your name, O Most High" (Psalm 92:1 NKJV).

TIPS FOR PRACTICING GRATITUDE

Your gratitude list does not need to be complex or lengthy, and the items on the list only need to matter to you:

- Write down goals. Dream.
- Make a practice out of telling the people around you what you appreciate about them.
- Write a thank you note to someone. Tell the person how much he or she has influenced your life.
- Look in the mirror and think about something you like about yourself.
- Read Ann Voskamp's book *One Thousand Gifts*, and start a gratitude journal.
- Pray, and count your blessings.
- Watch "Jessica's 'Daily Affirmation'" on YouTube.
- Make a mental list of three to five things for which you are truly grateful.

Today I spent the day alone at my computer, and yet I giggled with pleasure at the intermittent exchanges I had with my friends on Facebook. And I noticed myself being happy about those exchanges. Here's a list:

"I'm so thankful for this quiet time to sip coffee and relax."
"I found a great parking space."
"The snow didn't stick to the streets."

"I helped someone today."

"My mammogram was clear."

"I really enjoy the people I work with."

"My family loves me."

"I made it to the library before it closed."

"I enjoy my coworkers."

"My husband brought me coffee while I worked at my computer."

Make no mistake; life is difficult. But I have learned that we can make it better by implementing self-care, by making the commitment to renew ourselves. I have healed some emotional wounds, and have grieved and forgiven. I know who I am. I have learned to set boundaries with toxic people and with my time. I'm no longer so desperate to be loved that I say yes to everyone. I have learned to be my own best friend, and I'm at ease being alone. I have learned that I am flawed, as is everyone. I understand that showing vulnerability draws people close and that pretending to be perfect keeps them at bay. Play and exercise give me zest for life. I understand how important it is to surround myself with beauty and with people who love me. I know that generosity and gratitude fill me up more than they cost.

Whenever I am in the moment, just aware and grateful, I call it a "Maxwell House moment." I stopped by a fancy burger restaurant for dinner several years ago. I was sitting in a spot where I could look over the expanse of the restaurant, and I noticed so many interesting things. For example, there was the family where everyone was staring at their cell phones, texting rather than enjoying one another. I also noticed a couple in their fifties, who stole my focus. They sat across from each other, and even though the table was tiny, it was too long for their love. They clung to each other's fingertips, gazing at each other and talking. After watching the little children proudly carrying out their balloons, I saw my son. On that night he was the "bird helper"—that means he didn't let anyone mess with the restaurant's bird mascot.

I tilted my head behind the palm in a planter so he wouldn't see me staring. My memory took me back seventeen years to when that big guy was a toddler. I remember when the bird used to entertain him. I watched with pride as he greeted the customers with a smile, nodding and shaking hands with children, and then gently leading the redbird along. It's times like these when you choose to settle down and just "be," not wishing you were someone else or somewhere else. This is when happiness takes hold.

My hope and prayer for you is that you will take the next steps toward caring for and renewing yourself. I think you will find that gratitude will be your response from a full and happy soul.

I would maintain that thanks are the highest form of thought; and that gratitude is happiness doubled by wonder.

—G. K. Chesterton

BIBLIOGRAPHY

Allender, Dan. *The Wounded Heart: Hope for Adult Victims of Childhood Sexual Abuse*. Colorado Springs: NavPress, 2008.

Baumgardner, Barbara. *A Passage through Grief*. Nashville: Broadman & Holman, 1997.

Brown, Brené. "The Power of Vulnerability." www.youtube.com/watch?v=iCvmsMzlF7o

Brown, Stuart. "Play Is More Than Fun." www.ted.com/talks/stuart_brown_says_play_is_more_than_fun_it_s_vital.html.

Buckingham, Marcus. *Find Your Strongest Life: What the Happiest and Most Successful Women Do Differently*. Nashville: Thomas Nelson, 2009.

Buechner, Frederick. *Wishful Thinking: A Seeker's ABC*. San Francisco: HarperSanFrancisco, 1993.

Christakis, Nicholas A., and James H. Fowler. *Connected: The Surprising Power of Our Social Networks and How They Shape Our Lives*. New York: Little, Brown, 2009.

Cloud, Henry. *Changes That Heal: How to Understand Your Past to Ensure a Healthier Future*. Grand Rapids: Zondervan, 1993.

Cron, Ian Morgan. *Chasing Francis: A Pilgrim's Tale*. Colorado Springs: NavPress, 2006.

de Pomiane, Edourd. *French Cooking in Ten Minutes: Adapting to the Rhythm of Modern Life*. 1930; reprint, New York: North Point, 1994.

Deresiewicz, William. "Solitude and Leadership." *American Scholar* 79, no. 2 (2010): 20–31. Online: http://theamericanscholar.org/solitude-and-leadership/.

Doidge, Norman. *The Brain That Changes Itself: Stories of Personal Triumph from the Frontiers of Brain Science*. New York: Penguin, 2007.

Dorfman, Andrea. "How to Be Alone." www.youtube.com/watch?v=k7X7sZzSXYs.

Eldredge, John. *Waking the Dead: The Glory of a Heart Fully Alive*. Nashville: Thomas Nelson, 2003.

Epstein, Mark. *Open to Desire: Embracing a Lust for Life*. New York: Gotham, 2005.

Evans, Rachel Held. "A Little Mindfulness Never Hurt Anyone." http://rachelheldevans.com/article-1208637252.

Fox, John. "When Someone Deeply Listens to You." www.poeticmedicine.org/poetry.html.

Frankl, Viktor. *Man's Search for Meaning*. 1952; reprint, Boston: Beacon, 2006.

Funderberg, Lisa. "How to Be an Optimist," www.oprah.com/spirit/Optimism/1.

Harding, Matt. "Where the Hell Is Matt?" www.youtube.com/watch?v=zlfKdbWwruY.

InStep Ministries. "Are You Ready for a Relationship?" www.instepministries.com/quiz-relationship.php.

"Jessica's 'Daily Affirmation.'" www.youtube.com/watch?v=qR3rKOkZFkg.

Kenyon, Jane. "Otherwise." In *Collected Poems*. St. Paul: Graywolf, 2005.

Long, Christopher R., and James Averill. "Solitude: An Exploration of Benefits of Being Alone." *Journal for the Theory of Social Behaviour* 33:1 (2003): 21–44.

Martindale, Wayne, and Jerry Root, eds. *The Quotable Lewis*. Carol Stream, Ill.: Tyndale House, 1989.

McClellan, Stephanie, and Beth Hamilton. *So Stressed: The Ultimate Stress-Relief Plan for Women*. New York: Free Press, 2010.

Merton, Thomas. *No Man Is an Island.* New York: Harcourt, Brace, 1955.

Miller, Alice. *The Drama of the Gifted Child: The Search for the True Self.* Translated by Ruth Ward. New York: BasicBooks, 2007.

Moore, Thomas. *Care of the Soul: A Guide for Cultivating Depth and Sacredness in Everyday Life.* New York: HarperPerennial, 1994.

Mother Teresa. *A Gift for God: Prayers and Meditations.* San Francisco: HarperSanFrancisco, 1996.

Muller, Wayne. *How, Then, Shall We Live? Four Simple Questions That Reveal the Beauty and Meaning of Our Lives.* New York: Bantam, 1997.

———. *Sabbath: Finding Rest, Renewal, and Delight in Our Busy Lives.* New York: Bantam, 1999.

Mullins, Rich. "Pursuit of a Legacy." www.kidbrothers.net/video.html.

Neeld, Elizabeth Harper. *A Sacred Primer: The Essential Guide to Quiet Time and Prayer.* Nashville: Abingdon Press, 2005.

Nouwen, Henri. *Bread for the Journey: A Daybook of Wisdom and Faith.* San Francisco: HarperSanFrancisco, 1997.

Pennebaker, James W. *Opening Up: The Healing Power of Expressing Emotions.* New York: Guilford, 1997.

Pipher, Mary. *Reviving Ophelia: Saving the Selves of Adolescent Girls.* New York: Putnam, 1994.

Rath, Tom. *StrengthsFinder 2.0.* New York: Gallup, 2007.

Seligman, Martin E. P., et al. "Positive Education: Positive Psychology and Classroom Interventions." *Oxford Review of Education* 35, no. 3 (June 2009): 293–311.

Tournier, Paul. *To Understand Each Other.* Translated by John S. Gilmour. Richmond, Va.: John Knox, 1967.

Tronick, Edward. "The Still Face Experiment." www.youtube.com/watch?v=apzXGEbZht0

Winfrey, Oprah. "Oprah Talks to Elie Wiesel." www.oprah.com/omagazine/Oprah-Interviews-Elie-Wiesel/2.